IMPRESSIONS OF
GREAT NATURALISTS

My dear Aileen;

Upon their early Rose Living Persons.

L.T.O.

July 13th 1927
Castle Rock
Garrison-on-Hudson.

IMPRESSIONS OF
GREAT NATURALISTS

REMINISCENCES OF
DARWIN, HUXLEY, BALFOUR, COPE
AND OTHERS

BY

HENRY FAIRFIELD OSBORN

RESEARCH PROFESSOR OF ZOOLOGY IN COLUMBIA UNIVERSITY; SENIOR GEOLOGIST IN
UNITED STATES GEOLOGICAL SURVEY; PRESIDENT OF THE
AMERICAN MUSEUM OF NATURAL HISTORY

ILLUSTRATED WITH PORTRAITS

CHARLES SCRIBNER'S SONS
NEW YORK · LONDON
1924

TO

THE MEMORY OF

THE NATURALISTS, EXPLORERS, AND AUTHORS

WHOSE CREATIVE LIVES

ARE BRIEFLY TOUCHED UPON HERE

". . . those immortal dead who live again
In minds made better by their presence: live
In pulses stirr'd to generosity,
In deeds of daring rectitude, in scorn
For miserable aims that end with self,
In thoughts sublime that pierce the night like stars,
And with their mild persistence urge man's search
To vaster issues."

—GEORGE ELIOT

AUTOBIOGRAPHIC FOREWORD

THERE is no joy like the joy of creative work. To my mind all great men are creative, and among the greatest men are the creative naturalists from Aristotle to Darwin, whose self-effacing lives and enduring works are our most precious possessions. I like a naturalist better than a scientist, because there is less of the ego in him, and in a naturalist like Darwin the ego entirely disappears and through his vision we see Nature with the least human aberration. These "Impressions" may show the young and aspiring naturalists of our day that in the highest creative vision there is the least of self and the most of Nature. In the twelve lives chosen from the fifty-seven men and women of whom I have written,[1] I include Roosevelt, Bryce and Butler because as intrepid explorers and observers they show some of the highest qualities of the naturalist.

I had the good fortune to lead my student life between 1873 and 1880 under the spirit-

---

[1] The author has written fifty-seven biographic sketches, forty of which are listed in the appendix of this volume.

ual, moral, and intellectual influence of the great men of the Victorian age, the poets Wordsworth and Tennyson, as well as the natural philosophers Wallace, Darwin, Huxley, and Cope. The scientific thought of the first half of the nineteenth century was permeated with the theism of the Special Creation theory of the universe. In those fateful days of intellectual doubt between the false theism of Special Creation and the true theism of Evolution, I fortunately came under the influence of a series of broad-minded teachers, of Arnold Guyot in geology, of James McCosh in psychology and philosophy, of William M. Sloane in the philosophy of Kant, of William H. Welch in anatomy and the study of the Cell; of each of these incomparable teachers I like to recall that "I too sat at the feet of Gamaliel." McCosh numbered me in his favorite group of "eager young men" with the embryonic geologist Scott and the embryonic philosopher Ormond. Inspired with self-confidence by him in 1878, I took up original research in psychology and prepared a questionnaire on visual memory in cooperation with Francis Galton, cousin of Charles Darwin, publishing four psychological papers at the same time that I was writing my first palæontological papers on fossil mammals discovered in the Rocky Mountains in 1877–1878. This work also fitted me to write, ten years later, "From the Greeks to Darwin," my inaugural lectures in the Columbia University Professorship of Biology, the first of a series of volumes which I edited. While McCosh, to whom I dedicated this philosophical work, was eager and impetuous and urged the beginning of observation and research at once, Arnold Guyot, distinguished in the glaciology of Switzerland, taught that the way of learning is long and very arduous. I well recall the motto he gave me when I was groaning over the interminable difficulties of preparing fossils, a motto derived from Hippocrates and the patient Romans:

Art is long and difficult; criticism is short and easy.

This indeed is the message of Geology to the student mind and the underlying reason why Charles Lyell, a geologist, became the master of Charles Darwin, a biologist. Only from the eternal truths of the earth's past history can the immediate present of Life be understood.

Two of my eager Princeton comrades felt

the need of anatomy as much as I did, and without the aid of a teacher we started the dissection of a fish, guided by Huxley's "Comparative Anatomy of the Vertebrates." This laborious work on the porgy was followed by an anatomical escapade on the limb of *Homo sapiens*, part of a human cadaver, in one of the unused rooms of the Astronomical Observatory which we converted into a dissecting-room. The venerable astronomer, Professor Stephen Alexander, wondered at the source of the strange odors that filled the observatory, but never discovered the cause! These untaught and surreptitious studies in anatomy led to my coming, in the autumn of 1878, under one of the greatest teachers of anatomy this country has produced, William H. Welch, then a junior officer in the Bellevue Medical College. Fresh from the leading laboratories of Germany, Welch used the Teutonic method I had not known before, of introducing each of his discourses on the various kinds of cells with an historical review of discovery, showing how step by step one discovery in science leads to another. I felt for the first time the inspiration of the special virtue of German research, the most thorough and painstaking the world has ever known, the virtue of *grundlichkeit*, of going to the very bottom of things. Thus were drawing to a close my six American years when the question of whether I should go to Germany or to England was decided by a letter from Kitchen Parker, the distinguished English comparative anatomist and friend of Huxley, who personally advised me to go to London to study under Huxley and to Cambridge to study under Balfour.

Never shall I forget my first impression of Francis Maitland Balfour as I met him in the great court of Trinity College of Cambridge, in the spring of 1879, to apply for admission to his course in embryology. At the time he was twenty-eight years of age and I was twenty-one. I felt that I was in the presence of a superior being, of a type to which I could never possibly attain, and I did not lose this impression throughout the spring months in which he lectured on comparative embryology at Cambridge and in which we enjoyed many long afternoons of bicycle riding on the level roads of the Fens. I always felt that Balfour lived in a higher atmosphere, in another dimension of intellectual space.

Not that he was aloof—far from it, for he
was always in closest and most generous touch
with the minds of his students; he made you
feel that you had a mind and that your opinion and observation were of value, although
you knew all the while that your mind was
still embryonic and your opinions of the most
tentative order. His was by far the most balanced mind among all the English biologists.
He was at the time absorbed in embryology,
which was the reigning biological discipline
of the day. His untimely death in the Swiss
Alps in the year 1882 was a tragic loss, because English biologic thought soon entered
the long period of confusion and lack of bal-
ance that have characterized it to the present
time. The other great lesson taught by Balfour was that of the balanced daily life: the
morning lecture and tour of the laboratory,
the five quiet hours devoted to his own writing and research, the vigorous afternoon exercise, and the delightful care-free and shop-
free evening. At the time Balfour was turning out the great volumes of his "Comparative
Embryology," a monumental work, I asked
him how many hours a day he gave to writing;
he replied: "Never more than five hours."

A fresh mind is far more creative than a jaded mind.

In the autumn of 1879 I moved to London, which was then in the full and glorious tide of Victorian life. Not a member had fallen out of the great ranks. I had the good fortune to hear in the scientific societies some of these great men, such as Clark Maxwell in physics, to meet all the leading biologists except Wallace, and especially to come under the commanding personal influence of Huxley. Huxley especially imparted philosophic breadth, grasp of the whole subject, the force and value of expression, the wisdom and perception that come from survey of a very broad field, from both the philosophic and the anatomical standpoint. His sense of humor was delightful and brightened many of the most difficult passages in his discourses. By his way of living and by the unlimited personal sacrifices he made he taught me that we men of science must do our part in public education. To public service Huxley sacrificed his life, for not long after his great lecture course of 1879–1880, which I attended and of which I took the fullest notes, he broke down in health. When I last met him in Cambridge, at the British Association meeting of 1894, he shook his head sadly and said: "Osborn, I no longer can keep up with the progress of biology." Soon after his death, in 1895, I wrote the reminiscences which appear in this volume without change.

To Huxley I owe the greatest biological impression that came to me in England, namely, a few words with Charles Darwin in Huxley's laboratory. From the large number of students working there at the time, Huxley singled me out, perhaps because I was the only American, perhaps because of my early palæontological writing. I realized that I must make the most of the opportunity, and for a few moments I gazed steadily into Darwin's face and especially into his benevolent blue eyes, which were almost concealed below the overhanging brows, eyes that seemed to have a vision of the entire living world and that gave one the impression of translucent truthfulness. In my address at the Darwin Centenary at Cambridge I endeavored to convey this profound impression of translucent truthfulness. Darwin arrived at Evolution not because he desired to do so, but because he was forced into it by his own observations of Nature. He came of a long line of compellingly truthful ancestors, and certainly "truth, the whole truth, and nothing but the truth" is a distinctly English and Scotch trait. In my fifty years' experience with scientific men I have found them neither more nor less truthful than other men, because truthfulness does not go on all fours with genius, with powers of observation and of generalization. Darwin always kept in the realm of fact; he was equally sincere in the realm of opinion and of theory. If in the relatively small part of his life that he devoted to speculation and to theory his contributions are less permanent, it is because, after all, Nature is unreasonable and irrational in her methods.

On returning to America as a young comparative anatomist I was privileged to work as a comrade with men with whom I had started as a disciple. I became more intimate than ever with the Scotchman James McCosh and enjoyed his eager freshness of mind and desire to gain new ideas. For a gift on his eightieth birthday his students paraphrased the lines of Aristophanes: "Honor to the old man who in the declining vigor of years seeks to learn new subjects and to add to his wisdom." I had great reverence for another Scotchman, James Bryce, with his enthusiasm, his broad learning and experience, his eager reception of new ideas, to the very end of his life; finally, for that very unique Scotchman, John Muir. From their simple and hardy mode of living the Scotch contribute to the students of life enduring impressions of energy, vigor, youthfulness, and of the most genial and whole-hearted friendship.

In reprinting these "Impressions," extending over a very long period of years, from my youthful tribute to Balfour in 1883 to those of John Muir, John Burroughs, Theodore Roosevelt, and Howard Crosby Butler in the present decade, may I claim that years of observation have given me far deeper penetration into the sources of human character and personality? This penetration is due to my studies in heredity and my observations on the difference in races and racial characteristics, which, for example, separate the Scotch from the English and both from the Irish. Such penetration is carried as far as I am able to do at present in appreciation of the peculiar genius of John Muir and of John Burroughs. In contrasting these two friends I asked myself the question: "Why are they so much alike and why so different?" I believe I have partly answered this question, but we may go much farther in the sympathetic biographic analysis of the future. Since I wrote the first of my biographic studies, the principal titles of which are included in the appendix of this volume, I have been attempting to penetrate into human nature along a number of paths: first, along studies of heredity, already alluded to; second, along studies of the men of the Old Stone Age and their forebears; third, with the increasing conviction that our intellectual, moral, and spiritual reactions are extremely ancient and that they have been built up not in hundreds but in thousands—perhaps hundreds of thousands—of years. It would, however, take me far beyond the limits of a foreword to enter upon this deeper interpretation of the impressions and influences which great minds of great men of different kinds have exerted upon me.

In these "Impressions" I am not in any case attempting to portray the whole man, but only one principal aspect of each life.

The nearest approach to a full biographic treatment is the centenary address on the life and works of Charles Darwin and the memorial address on his comrade, Alfred Russel Wallace. It was an appreciation which I received in a letter from Wallace, reproduced in facsimile at the beginning of this volume, also letters from Mrs. Huxley and her son, from Lady Bryce, and from friends of John Burroughs and John Muir that first led me to believe that these biographical sketches would be helpful to young men and young women who aspire to greatness along different lines of intellectual endeavor. I have omitted many of my biographic essays because I was not confident that they would be of interest to laymen as well as to young scientists, to whom this work is addressed, but I cannot pass by two of my great palæontological predecessors, Joseph Leidy and Edward Drinker Cope, because the resemblances and contrasts between these two men are especially illuminating in scientific life.

Cope was certainly the most brilliant creative mind in comparative anatomy and evolution that America has produced. Quaker by birth, he was a fighter by nature, both in

theory and in fact. On one occasion, in the
American Philosophical Society, a difference
of opinion with his friend Persifor Frazer led
to such a violent controversy that the two
scientists retired to the hallway and came to
blows! On the following morning I happened
to meet Cope and could not help remarking
on a blackened eye. "Osborn," he said,
"don't look at my eye. If you think my eye
is black, you ought to see Frazer this morning!" But such differences of opinion did
not sever the lifelong friendship, and when
Cope died Frazer was the first to pay a glow-
ing tribute to his genius. Cope was not a
single but a multiple personality; he presents
the widest possible contrast to a retiring nature like that of Alfred Russel Wallace, a
sketch of whom opens this volume. Wallace,
the last survivor of the great trio of British
naturalists of the nineteenth century, survived
by only a few months another member of the
group, Sir Joseph Hooker, who introduced the
famous Darwin-Wallace papers on Natural
Selection to the Linnæan Society in 1858.
Lyell, Darwin, and Wallace were three successive but closely kindred spirits, whose
work began and ended with what will be

known as the second great epoch of evolutionary thought, the first being that of the
precursors of Darwin and the third that in
which we live. They established Evolution
through a continued line of attack by precisely similar methods of observation and
reasoning over an extremely broad field.

As to the closeness of the intellectual se-
quence between these three men, those who
know the original edition of the second volume of Lyell's "The Principles of Geology,"
published in 1832, must regard it as the second biologic classic of the century—the first
being Lamarck's "Philosophie Zoologique,"
of 1809—on which Darwin through his higher
and much more creative vision built up his
"Journal of Researches." When Lyell faltered
in the application of his own principles Darwin went on and was followed by Wallace.
The two older men may be considered to have
united in guiding the mind of Wallace, because the young naturalist, fourteen years the
junior of Darwin, took both "The Principles"
of Lyell and "The Journal" of Darwin with
him on his journey to South America, during
which his career fairly began.

From his record of observations during his

life in the tropics of America and of Asia Wallace will be remembered not only as one of the independent discoverers of the theory of Natural Selection but next to Darwin as one of the great naturalists of the nineteenth century. His range and originality are astounding in these days of specialization. His main lines of thought, although in many instances suggested to his mind somewhat suddenly, were developed and presented in a deliberate and masterly way through the series of papers and books extending from 1850 to 1913. The highest level of his creative life was, however, reached at the age of thirty-five, when with Darwin he published his sketch of the theory of Natural Selection. This outburst of original thought, on which his reputation will chiefly rest, came as an almost automatic generalization from his twelve years in the tropics.

The two most powerful men I have known intimately were J. Pierpont Morgan and Theodore Roosevelt. I had the privilege of calling the former "Uncle Pierpont" and have vivid recollections of him as he was in 1867, when I was a boy, and in the last two brilliant decades of his life. Theodore Roosevelt I

knew slightly as a boy, as an intimate friend
of my naturalist brother, Frederick, and in
the last two and great decades of his life as
my own friend. Although the man in the
street would say that no two Americans could
be further apart than these two, in many
characteristics they were closely similar. The
outstanding point of likeness was their courage in facing obstacles, their dominance in
overcoming difficulties of all kinds. There
was no "I can't" in the vocabulary of either
man; rather "I can and I will." Close contact with both of these men enforced the life
motto which became my own: *Whatever is
right can be done, and shall be done.* Powerful as both were in leadership, they always
sought the counsel of their friends and were apt
to be governed by it, unless it was the counsel
of timidity or of irresolution. Neither was
dominant in the sense that Woodrow Wil-
son was dominant and autistic—to use the
professional phrase. Both won the devoted
friendship and admiration of hundreds of men
and women, and both made many enemies;
through similar virtues Roosevelt became the
opponent of Morgan and Morgan became the
opponent of Roosevelt. Both were intensely

patriotic and willing to make any sacrifice,
however great, for their country. Both were
deeply religious and were guided by an unfaltering faith in Divine Providence. The
most surprising likeness I observed was their
humility; I never saw a trace of conceit in
either Pierpont Morgan or Theodore Roosevelt. The assurance and self-confidence they
both displayed in critical and commanding
moments were part of the great game of life.
Leaders must have broad shoulders, firm
necks, and confident and determined faces
when the world is full of doubting Thomases,
as it always is. A marked point of likeness
was the power of immediate, almost instan-
taneous, decision, which sometimes led both
men astray. Contrasting with their power
of command were their simplicity, their un-
selfish devotion to their friends, and their love
of children and fascination for children. Both
had a deep interest in science; with Morgan
it was mathematics, minerals, and gems, and,
in later years, archæology. Natural history
was the first and last love of Theodore Roosevelt, in all its branches, and special study of
birds and mammals constituted the greatest
pleasure of his life.

It will surprise many of my readers that I
have instituted such a comparison, that I
have found resemblances amidst the many
violent contrasts in the lives and characters
of these two great Americans. It was the
love of nature and of human nature which
made them alike. Few of us are single in our
personalities; most of us are dual, and the
rare men like Morgan and Roosevelt are multiple. Among great naturalists Wallace, Darwin, and Pasteur were men of single natures,
whose whole lives were devoted to single great
purposes, to the attainment of which all other
objects in life gave way. They were neither
combatant nor militant, nor did they ever
seek to force their theories or opinions by
militant methods. They sought seclusion,
avoided public meetings and controversies,
and were astonished by the world-wide ac-
claim of their discoveries. It is told of Darwin that after meeting Gladstone he expressed
surprise that such a very great man had paid
him so much attention. It appears that this
simplicity of life and avoidance of renown are
most favorable to that creative state of mind
which most frequently engenders renown.

On the other hand, Huxley and Cope were,
above all, combatants in the new social and

philosophical arena of Evolution. Huxley's world-wide fame rests partly on his defense of freedom of thought and of research and on the brilliance of his rapier-like thrusts at some of the shams and hypocrisies of the Special Creation exponents of his day. His genius lay in polemics, in criticism, in exposition, rather than in creative discovery and generalization; it is a striking fact that he did not add a single new principle to the philosophy of Evolution. His life was one of enforced activity and public service, which left him little or no repose for creative thought, yet he added to anatomy a number of very important generalizations. There is no measuring what Huxley might have done if he had enjoyed the repose that was granted to Darwin. Cope was, above all, a creative naturalist of a high order, with a rapidity and originality of thought almost without parallel in the history of anatomy; great generalizations affecting the order and arrangement of the whole kingdom of back-boned animals arose from his brain, while in philosophical analysis he was a tyro where Huxley was a master.

From these impressions of the lives of many naturalists we see that the naturalist is animated first of all by the joy of observation, without initial hope or thought of discovery but surely in the end leading to discovery; leading also to creative thought if observation is pursued with a single eye and unfaltering purpose, regardless of all obstacles or dangers and of the greatest impediment of all, namely, interest in self and in self-advancement.

CONTENTS

CONTENTS

ACKNOWLEDGMENT

"The Life and Works of Darwin" was an address delivered at Columbia University on February 12, 1909, the hundredth anniversary of Darwin's birth, as the first of a series of nine lectures on Charles Darwin and his influence on science. "The Darwin Centenary" is based on an address in reply to the reception of delegates at Cambridge. "A Student's Reminiscences of Huxley" was a lecture delivered at the Marine Biological Laboratory of Wood's Hole in the summer session of 1895. The address on James Bryce was delivered at the memorial service to Viscount Bryce at the Cathedral of St. John the Divine, March 5, 1922. The address on Joseph Leidy was originally delivered at the Joseph Leidy Centenary, Philadelphia, December 6, 1923, and was later published in *Science*. The article on Howard Crosby Butler was an address delivered at the Graduate College of Princeton University, October 31, 1922. This address was afterward published in the Butler memorial volume by the Princeton University Press. The chapter on John Burroughs is an address which was delivered at the John Burroughs memorial meeting, American Academy of Arts and Letters, on November 18, 1921.

Other chapters of this book are based on articles published in the following magazines: *Popular Science Monthly, Science, The Century, The Sierra Club Bulletin.*

ALFRED RUSSEL WALLACE

ALFRED RUSSEL WALLACE
1823–1913

I never had the pleasure of meeting Wallace, but I felt rewarded for the time I devoted to the study of his works and the influences which shaped his great career in preparing this Impression by his letter of acknowledgment, which is reproduced in facsimile. Wallace was a great man, although he was overshadowed by a much greater man, Darwin. The scientific relations of these two men were ideal; their magnanimity toward each other in the crisis of independent discovery of the great principle of Natural Selection is one of the noblest episodes in the history of biology.

ALFRED RUSSEL WALLACE

NATURE and nurture conspire to form a naturalist. Predisposition, an opportune period, and a happy series of events favored Alfred Russel Wallace.

Wallace was the son of Thomas Vere Wallace, of Hanworth, Middlesex, England, and Mary Anne Grennell, of Hertford. His ancestry is obscure. On the paternal side he is probably descended from one of the branches of Sir William Wallace, the popular national hero of Scotland, but nothing is known back of his grandfather, who was probably keeper of the inn on the estates of the Duke of St. Albans, of Hanworth. The burial records of Hanworth mention an Admiral James Wallace. In his mother's family on the paternal side is the name Greenell, of Hertford, probably the "Greenaile" in 1579, French Huguenot refugees after the massacre of St. Bartholomew. Her grandfather was for many years alderman and twice mayor of Hertford. One of the Greenells was an architect.

Wallace's father took up the profession of the law, but did not continue, and up to his marriage lived the life of a fairly well-to-do middle-class gentleman. After his marriage he essayed the publishing of two magazines apparently devoted to art, antiquities and general literature, which were failures. He then moved from Marylebone to more rural districts where living was less expensive, first to St. Georges, Southwark, and then to Usk, Monmouthshire. In this village Alfred Russel Wallace was born on January 8, 1823.

When Wallace was about six years of age the family moved to Hertford, where his education was begun in the old grammar school that dated back to 1617. He left school too young to begin Greek, but he studied Latin, and next to Latin grammar the most painful subject he learned was geography, principally because of the meaningless way in which it was taught. During the last year of study at the grammar school, as the family were then in very straitened circumstances, he assisted in the teaching of the younger boys in reading, arithmetic, and writing.

Wallace considered that his home life in Hertford was in many ways more educational than the time spent at school. His father was a man who enjoyed the pleasure of literature and belonged to a book club through which a constant stream of interesting books came to the house, from which he read aloud to the family in the evenings. The father earned a small income tutoring and as librarian of a small library, and the son Alfred spent hours reading there, also.

At the age of thirteen young Wallace left school, with a view to learning land surveying. He stayed in London a short time with his brother John, who was apprenticed to a master builder, and their evenings were most frequently spent in the "Hall of Science," a kind of mechanics institute for advanced thinkers among workmen. Here he heard many lectures by Robert Owen, the founder of the socialist movement in England, and took up philosophical reading, beginning with Paine's "Age of Reason," among other books. In the summer of 1837 he went with his brother William into Bedfordshire to begin his education as a land surveyor, and practised for seven years in various parts of England and Wales.

After a time it was decided that he should try to pursue the clock-making business as well as surveying and general engineering,

and Wallace considered that this was the first
of several turning-points in his life, because
changes in the business of the clock-making
concern with which he was connected at
Leighton prevented his continuing this work
for more than a short period. He was delighted to take up again in 1839 the employment of land surveying because of the oppor-
tunities it afforded for out-of-door life.

While at Neath, in Wales, there was not
much demand for surveying, and Wallace
occupied himself in constructing a rude telescope with which he was able to observe the
moon and Jupiter's satellites, and he developed much interest in studying astronomy
and in the development of astronomical in-
struments. But he says that he was chiefly
occupied with what became more and more
the solace and delight of his lonely rambles
among the moors and mountains, namely, his
first introduction to the variety, the beauty
and the mystery of nature as manifested in
the vegetable kingdom.

His earnings were very meagre and he had
little money for the purchase of books. During the seven years he worked with his brother
he says he "hardly ever had more than a few

shillings for personal expenses." It was during this period, while most occupied out of doors with the observation and collection of plants, that he began to write down more or less systematically his ideas on various subjects that interested him. His first literary efforts all bear dates of the autumn and winter of 1843, when he was between twenty and twenty-one years of age. One of his first productions was the rough sketch of a popular lecture on botany addressed to an audience supposed to be as ignorant as he was when he began his observation of the native flowers. A second of these early lectures was on the subject "The Advantages of Varied Knowledge," which he considered of interest chiefly as showing the bent of his mind at the time and indicating a disposition for discursive reading and study. He also wrote at this time on the manners and customs of the Welsh peasantry in Brecknockshire and Glamorganshire, and put the matter in form for one of the London magazines, but it was declined.

These early and serious studies in botany, continuing for four years, prepared him for the plant wonders of the tropics. At the age of twenty-one he went to London. He afterward regarded his difficulty in obtaining employment as a great turning-point in his career, "for otherwise," he writes, "it seems very unlikely that I should ever have undertaken what at that time seemed rather a wild scheme, a journey to the almost unknown forests of the Amazon in order to observe nature and make a living by collecting."

In his autobiographic volumes of 1905, "My Life, a Record of Events and Opinions," there is also an interesting sketch of his state of mind at this time.

I do not think that at this formative period I could be said to have shown special superiority in any of the higher mental faculties, but I possessed a strong desire to know the causes of things, a great love of beauty in form and color, and a considerable, but not excessive desire for order and arrangement in whatever I had to do. If I had one distinct mental faculty more prominent than another it was the power of correct reasoning from a review of the known facts in any case to the causes or laws which produced them, and also in detecting fallacies in the reasoning of other persons.

Elsewhere in his autobiography he observes that whatever reputation in science, literature and thought he may possess is the result of the organs of comparison, causality and order, with firmness, acquisitiveness, concentrativeness, constructiveness and wonder, all above the average, but none of them excessively developed, combined with a moderate faculty of language which

enables me to express my ideas and conclusions in writing though but imperfectly in speech. I feel, myself, how curiously and persistently these faculties have acted in various combinations to determine my tastes, disposition and actions.

Wallace shared Darwin's strong sentiment for justice as between man and man, and abhorrence of tyranny and unnecessary interference with the liberty of others. His retiring disposition enabled him to enjoy long periods of reflection, receptiveness and solitude, both at home and in the tropics, out of which have come the sudden illuminations or flashes of light leading to the solution of the problems before him. As to this wonderful mechanism of induction, Wallace observes:

I have long since come to see that no one deserves either praise or blame for the *ideas* that come to him, but only for the *actions* resulting

therefrom. Ideas and beliefs are certainly not
voluntary acts. They come to us—we hardly
know *how* or *whence*, and once they have got
possession of us we can not reject or change them
at will.

Apart from Darwin's education in Christ's
College, Cambridge, as compared with Wallace's self-education, the parallel between his
intellectual tendencies and environment and
those of Charles Darwin is extraordinary.
They enjoyed a similar current of influence
from men, from books and from nature. Thus
the next turning-point in his life was his
meeting with Henry Walter Bates, through
whom he acquired his zest for the wonders of
insect life, which opened for the first time for
him the zoological windows of nature. In a
measure Bates was to Wallace what the Reverend John S. Henslow had been to Darwin.
It is noteworthy that the greater and most
original part of his direct observations of
nature was upon the adaptations of insects.

Darwin and Wallace fell under the spell of
the same books, first and foremost those of
Lyell, as noted above, then of Humboldt in
his "Personal Narrative" (1814-18), of Robert Chambers in his "Vestiges of the Natural

History of Creation" (1844), of Malthus in his "Essay on the Principle of Population" (1798).

It was, however, Darwin's own "Journal of Researches," published in 1845, and read by Wallace at the age of twenty-three, which determined him to invite Bates to accompany him on his journey to the Amazon and Rio Negro, which filled the four years 1848-52. In this wondrous equatorial expanse, like Darwin he was profoundly impressed with the forests, the butterflies and birds, and with his first meeting with man in an absolute state of nature. Bates, himself a naturalist of high order,[1] was closely observing the mimetic resemblances among insects to animate and inanimate objects and introducing Wallace to a field which he subsequently made his own. Bates remained several years after Wallace's departure and published his classical memoir on mimicry in 1860–61. Wallace's own description of his South American experiences, entitled "Narrative of Travels on the Amazon," published in 1853 when he was thirty years of age, does not display the

---

[1] See his principal work, entitled "Naturalist on the River Amazons," 2 vols., 8vo, John Murray, London. 1863.

ability of his later writings and shows that his powers were slowly developing.

His eight years of travel between 1854 and 1862 in the Indo-Malay Islands, the Timor Group, Celebes, the Moluccas and the Papuan Group brought his powers to full maturity. It is apparent that his prolonged observations on the natives, the forests, the birds and mammals, and especially on the butterflies and beetles, were gradually storing his mind for one of those discharges of generalization which come so unexpectedly out of the vast accumulation of facts. "The Malay Archipelago" of 1869, published seven years after the return, is Wallace's "journal of researches," that is, it is to be compared with Darwin's great work of this title. Its fine breadth of treatment in anthropology, zoology, botany and physiography gives it a rank second only to Darwin's "Journal" in a class of works repeatedly enriched by British naturalists from the time of Burchell's journey in Africa.

Wallace's first trial at the evolution problem was his essay sent to the *Annals and Magazine of Natural History* in 1855, entitled "On the Law Which Has Regulated the Introduction of New Species." This paper suggested the *when* and *where* of the occurrence of new forms, but not the *how*. He concludes:

It has now been shown, though most briefly and imperfectly, how the law that *"Every species has come into existence coincident both in time and space with a preexisting closely allied species,"* connects together and renders intelligible a vast number of independent and hitherto unexplained facts.

In February, 1858, during a period of intermittent fever at Ternate, the *how* arose in his mind with the recollection of the "Essay" of Malthus, and there flashed upon him all the possible effects of the struggle for existence. Twenty years before the same idea, under similar circumstances, had come into the mind of Darwin. The parallel is extraordinary as shown in the following citations:

DARWIN	WALLACE
In October, 1838, that is, fifteen months after I had begun my systematic inquiry, I happened to read for amusement, "Malthus on Population," and being well prepared to appreciate the struggle for existence which everywhere goes on from long-continued observations of the habits of animals and plants, it at once struck me that under these circumstances favorable variations would tend to be preserved, and unfavorable ones to	In February, 1858, I was suffering from a rather severe attack of intermittent fever at Ternate, in the Moluccas; and one day, while lying on my bed during the cold fit, wrapped in blankets, though the thermometer was at 88° Fahr., the problem again presented itself to me, and something led me to think of the "positive checks" described by Malthus in his "Essay on Population," a work I had read several years before, and which

be destroyed. *The result of this would be the formation of new species.* Here, then, I had at last got a theory by which to work; but I was so anxious to avoid prejudice that I determined not for some time to write even the briefest sketch of it. In June, 1842, I first allowed myself the satisfaction of writing a very brief abstract of my theory in pencil, in thirty-five pages, and this was enlarged during the summer of 1844 into one of 230 pages.—Darwin's "Autobiography," Chap. II.

had made a deep and **permanent** impression on my mind. These checks—war, disease, famine and the like—must, it occurred to me, act on animals as well as man. Then I thought of the enormously rapid multiplication of animals, causing these checks to be much more effective in them than in the case of man; and while pondering vaguely on this fact there suddenly flashed upon me the *idea* of the survival of the fittest—that the individuals removed by these checks must be on the whole inferior to those that survived. In the two hours that elapsed before my ague fit was over, I had thought out almost the whole of the theory; and the same evening I sketched the draft of my paper, and in the two succeeding evenings wrote it out in full, and sent it by the next post to Mr. Darwin.—Wallace's "My Life," p. 212.

Darwin had been working upon the verification of the same idea for twenty years. We owe to Sir Joseph Hooker and to Lyell the bringing together of these independent but strikingly similar manuscripts. The noble episode which followed of the joint publication of the discovery was prophetic of the continued care for truth and carelessness of self, of the friendship, mutual admiration and co-operation between these two high-minded men, which affords a golden example for our own and future ages.   Each loved his own creations, yet undervalued his own work; each accorded enthusiastic praise to the work of the other.

It is a striking circumstance in the history of biology that Wallace's rapidly produced sketch of 1858 "On the Tendencies of Varieties to Part Indefinitely from the Original Type" not only pursues a line of thought parallel to that of Darwin, except in excluding the analogy of natural with human selection, but embodies the permanent substance of the selection theory as it is today after fifty-four years of world-wide research.   It may be regarded as his masterpiece.   The attempt has been made by De Vries and others to show that Wallace in his "Darwinism" of 1889 differed from Darwin on important points, but whatever may be true of this final modification of the theory, a very careful comparison of the Darwin-Wallace sketches of 1858 shows that they both involve the principle of discontinuity; in fact, fluctuation in the sense of plus and minus variation was not recognized at the time; the notion of variation was that derived directly from field rather than from laboratory notes. This is repeatedly implied in Wallace's language and especially in his sketch of 1858:

. . . there is a general principle in nature which will cause many *varieties* to survive the parent species, and to give rise to successive variations departing further and further from the original type, and which also produces, in domesticated animals, the tendency of varieties to return to the parent form. . . .

Most or perhaps all the variations from the typical form of a species must have some definite effect, however slight, on the habits or capacities of the individuals. Even a change of color might, by rendering them more or less distinguishable, affect their safety; a greater or less development of hair might modify their habits. . . . The superior variety would then alone remain, and on a return to favorable circumstances would rapidly increase in numbers and occupy the place of the extinct species and variety.

The *variety* would now have replaced the *species*, of which it would be a more perfectly developed and more highly organized form. . . . Here, then, we have *progression and continued divergence* deduced from the general laws which regulate the existence of animals in a state of nature, and from the undisputed fact that varieties do frequently occur. . . . Variations in unimportant parts might also occur, having no perceptible effect on the life-preserving powers; and the varieties so furnished might run a course parallel with the parent species, either giving rise to further variations or returning to the former type. . . . In the wild animal, on the contrary, all its faculties and powers being brought into full action for the necessities of existence, any increase becomes immediately available, is strengthened by exercise, and must even slightly modify the food, the habits and the whole economy of the race. It creates, as it were, a new animal, one of superior powers, and which will necessarily increase in numbers and outlive those inferior to it. . . .

We see, then, that no inferences as to varieties in a state of nature can be deduced from the observation of those occurring among domestic animals. . . . Domestic animals are abnormal, irregular, artificial; they are subject to varieties which never occur and never can occur in a state of nature; their very existence depends altogether on human care. . . . An origin such as is here advocated will also agree with the peculiar character of the modifications of form and structure which obtain in organized beings—the many lines of divergence from a central type, the increasing efficiency and power of a particular organ through a succession of allied species, and the remarkable persistence of unimportant parts, such as color, texture of plumage and hair, form of horns or crests, through a series of species differing considerably in more essential characters. . . . This progression, by minute steps, in various directions, but always checked and balanced by the necessary conditions, subject to which alone existence can be preserved, may, it is believed, be followed out so as to agree with all the phenomena. . . .

It is true that Wallace subsequently modi-
fied his theory, adopted the selection of plus
and minus fluctuations, and became a determined opponent of the mutation hypothesis
of De Vries.

The distinctive features of the later development of the theory in Wallace's mind were
his more implicit faith in selection, his insis-
tence on utility or selection value of new or
varying characters, his flat rejection of La-
marckism, his reliance on spontaneous variations as supplying all the materials for selection. This confidence appears in the following
passages from his militant reply in the volume
of 1889 to the critics of Darwinism:

The right or favorable variations are so frequently present that the unerring power of natural
selection never wants materials to work upon. . . .
Weismann's theory . . . adds greatly to the importance of natural selection as the one invariable and ever-present factor in all organic change
and that which can alone have produced the tem-
porary fixity combined with the secular modification of species.

The principle of discontinuity is less clearly
brought out than in the first sketch of 1858;
the selection of fluctuation is favorably con-

sidered. The laws and causes of variation are, however, assumed rather than taken up as a subject of inquiry. These opinions of 1889 were the summation of twenty-nine years of work.

To return to the life-narrative, the autumn of 1860 found Wallace in the Moluccas reading the "Origin of Species" through five or six times, each time with increasing admiration. A letter of September 1 to his friend George Silk contains the key to the subsequent direction of his research, namely, his recognition of the vast breadth of Darwin's principles and his determination to devote his life to their exposition:

I could *never have approached* the completeness of his book, its vast accumulation of evidence, its overwhelming argument, and its admirable tone and spirit. I really feel thankful that it has *not* been left to me to give the theory to the world. Mr. Darwin has created a new science and a new philosophy; and I believe that never has such a complete illustration of a new branch of human knowledge been due to the labors and researches of a single man. Never have such vast masses of widely scattered and hitherto quite unconnected facts been combined into a system and brought to bear upon the establishment of such a grand and new and simple philosophy.

The discovery of "Natural Selection" again turned the course of Wallace's life. In his autobiography he writes:

I had, in fact, been bitten with the passion for species and their description, and if neither Darwin nor myself had hit upon "natural selection," I might have spent the best years of my life in this comparatively profitless work, but the new ideas swept all this away. . . . This outline of the paper will perhaps enable my readers to understand the intense interest I felt in working out all these strange phenomena, and showing how they could almost all be explained by that law of "Natural Selection" which Darwin had discovered many years before, and which I also had been so fortunate as to hit upon.

The coloring of animals as observed in the tropics and the Malayan Islands was the subject in which Wallace made his most extensive and original contributions to Darwinism. In his sketch of 1858 he wrote:

Even the peculiar colors of many animals, especially insects, so closely resembling the soil or the leaves or the trunks on which they habitually reside, are explained on the same principle; for though in the course of ages varieties of many tints may have occurred, *yet those races having colors best adapted to concealment from their enemies would inevitably survive the longest.*

Returning from the Archipelago in 1862, he published in 1864 his pioneer paper, "The Malayan Papilionidæ or Swallow-tailed Butterflies, as illustrative of the Theory of Natural Selection," in which he at once took rank beside Bates and Müller as one of the great contributors to the color characteristics of animals. We see him step by step developing the ideas of protective resemblance which he had fully discussed with Bates, of alluring and warning colors, and of mimicry, pointing out the prevalence of mimicry in the female rather than in the male. The whole series of phenomena is believed to depend upon the great principle of the utility of every character, upon the need of color protection by almost all animals, and upon the known fact that no characteristic is so variable as color, that, therefore, concealment is most easily obtained by color modification. Protective resemblance in all its manifold forms has ever been dominant in his mind as a greater principle than that of the sexual selection of color which Darwin favored.

Here may be cited Wallace's own account

of his famous observation of mimicry in the
leaf butterfly from his volume of 1869, "The
Malay Archipelago":

The other species to which I have to direct attention is the *Kallima paralekta*, a butterfly of
the same family group as our Purple Emperor, and
of about the same size or larger. Its upper surface is of a rich purple, variously tinged with ash
color, and across the fore wings there is a broad
bar of deep orange, so that when on the wing it is
very conspicuous. This species was not uncommon
in dry woods and thickets, and I often endeavored to capture it without success, for after flying
a short distance it would enter a bush among
dry or dead leaves, and however carefully I
crept up to the spot I could never discover it
till it would suddenly start out again and then
disappear in a similar place. At length I was
fortunate enough to see the exact spot where the
butterfly settled, and though I lost sight of it
for some time, I at length discovered that it was
close before my eyes, but that in its position of
repose it so closely resembled a dead leaf attached
to a twig as almost certainly to deceive the eye
even when gazing full upon it. I captured several
specimens on the wing, and was able fully to understand the way in which this wonderful resemblance is produced. . . . All these varied details
combine to produce a disguise that is so complete
and marvellous as to astonish every one who observes it; and the habits of the insects are such as
to utilize all these peculiarities, and render them

available in such a manner as to remove all doubt of the purpose of this singular case of mimicry, which is undoubtedly a protection to the insect.

In 1867, in a manner which delighted Darwin, Wallace advanced his provisional solution of the cause of the gay and even gaudy colors of caterpillars as warnings of distastefulness. In 1868 he propounded his explanation of the colors of nesting birds, that when both sexes are conspicuously colored, the nest conceals the sitting bird, but when the male is conspicuously colored and the nest is open to view, the female is plainly colored and inconspicuous. His theory of recognition colors as of importance in enabling the young birds and mammals to find their parents was set forth in 1878, and he came to regard it as of very great importance.

In "Tropical Nature" (1878) the whole subject of the colors of animals in relation to natural and sexual selection is reviewed, and the general principle is brought out that the exquisite beauty and variety of insect colors has not been developed through their own visual perceptions, but mainly and perhaps exclusively through those of the higher animals which prey upon them. This conception

of color origin, rather than that of the general
influence of solar light and heat or the special
action of any form of environment, leads him
to his functional and biological classification
of the colors of living organisms into five
groups, which forms the foundation of the
modern, more extensive and critical classification of Poulton. He concluded (p. 172):

We find, then, that neither the general influence
of solar light and heat, nor the special action of
variously tinted rays, are adequate causes for the
wonderful variety, intensity and complexity of the
colors that everywhere meet us in the animal and
vegetable worlds. Let us, therefore, take a wider
view of these colors, grouping them into classes
determined by what we know of their actual
uses or special relations to the habits of their
possessors. This, which may be termed the
functional and biological classification of the colors
of living organisms, seems to be best expressed by
a division into five groups, as follows:

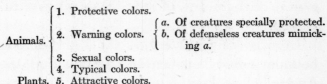

Animals.
1. Protective colors.
2. Warning colors.
  a. Of creatures specially protected.
  b. Of defenseless creatures mimick-
     ing a.
3. Sexual colors.
4. Typical colors.
Plants. 5. Attractive colors.

Twelve years later he devoted four chapters
of his "Darwinism" to the colors of animals
and plants, still maintaining the hypotheses

of utility, of spontaneous variation and of
selection.

The study of geographic distribution of
animals also sprang from the inspiration of
the Malayan journey and from the sugges-
tiveness of the eleventh and twelfth chapters
of "The Origin of Species," which Wallace
determined to work out in an exhaustive manner. Following the preliminary treatises of
Buffon, of Cuvier and Forbes, and the early
regional classification of Sclater, Wallace takes
rank as the founder of the science of zoogeography in his two great works, "The Geographical Distribution of Animals" of 1876, and
"Island Life" of 1881, the latter volume following the first as the result of four years of
additional thought and research. His early
observations on insular distribution were
sketched out in his article of 1860, "The Zoological Geography of the Malayan Archipelago."

Here is his discovery of the Bali-Lombok
boundary line between the Indian and the
Australian zoological regions which has since
been generally known by his name.

In these fundamental geologic and geographic works Wallace appears as a disciple

of Lyell in uniformitarianism, and a follower
of Dana as regards the stability and permanence of continental and oceanic areas, for
which doctrine he advances much original
evidence. He taxes his ingenuity to discover
every possible means of dispersal of animals
and plants other than those which would be
afforded by hypothetical land connections;
he considers every possible cause of extinction
other than those which are sudden or cata-
clysmal.

The "Island Life" is in itself a great contribution to zoology and zoogeography, the
starting-point of all modern discussion of insular faunas and floras. His conservative
theory of dispersal is applied in an original
way to explain the arctic element in the
mountain regions of the tropics, as opposed to
the low-temperature theory of tropical lowlands during the Glacial Period; his explanation is founded on known facts as to the dispersal and distribution of plants and does not
require the extreme changes in the climate of
tropical lowlands during the Glacial Period
on which Darwin founded his interpretation.
The causes and influence of the Glacial Epoch
are discussed in an exposition of Croll's theory.

In this connection may be mentioned one of Wallace's original geological contributions, in the article "Glacial Erosions of Lake Basins," published in 1893, namely, his theory of glacial erosion as a means of explaining the origin of valley lakes of glaciated countries.

The original trend of Wallace's thought as to the ascent of man is first shown in the three anthropological essays of 1864, 1869 and 1870, which were subsequently collected in the volume "Contributions to the Theory of Natural Selection." This work, published in 1871, includes all his original essays from 1855 to 1869 on selection, on color and human evolution, which foreshadow the later development of his speculative philosophy.

A suggestive anthropological contribution is the article entitled "The Expressiveness of Speech or Mouth Gesture as a Factor in the Origin of Language," in which is developed the theory of the origin of language in connection with the motions of the lips, jaws and tongue. With Wallace also arose the now widely accepted belief that the Australian aborigines constitute a low and perhaps primitive type of the Caucasian race.

In the article of 1864, "The Development

of Human Races under the Law of Natural Selection," Wallace first advanced the hypothesis which has since proved to be untenable, that so soon as man learned to use fire and make tools, to grow food, to domesticate animals, to use clothing and build houses, the action of natural selection was diverted from his body to his mind, and thenceforth his physical form remained stable, while his mental faculties improved. His subsequent papers on human evolution, "The Limits of Natural Selection as Applied to Man" of 1869, "On Instinct in Man and Animals" of 1871, mark the gradual divergence of his views from those of Darwin, for in his opinion natural selection is believed to be inadequate to account for several of the physical as well as psychical characteristics of man, for example his soft, sensitive skin, his speech, his color sense, his mathematical, musical and moral attributes. He concluded:

The inference I would draw from this class of phenomena is that a superior intelligence has guided the development of man in a definite direction, and for a special purpose, just as man guides the development of many animal and vegetable forms.

It is also prophetic of his later indictments of the so-called civilization of our times that we find at the end of the closing pages of "The Malay Archipelago" the first statement of the feeling which so many travelers have experienced from a comparison of the natural and so-called civilized condition of man that "social evolution from barbarism to civilization" has not advanced general human welfare. These humanitarian and partly socialistic ideas are developed in a series of recurrent essays between 1882 and 1903, including "The Nationalization of Land" and "Studies Scientific and Social."

He returned to this subject in what we believe to be his last published essay, namely, his "Social Environment and Moral Progress" of 1913, wherein he considers the so-called "feministic" movement and future of woman:

The foregoing statement of the effect of established natural laws, if allowed free play under rational conditions of civilization, clearly indicates that the position of woman in the not distant future will be far higher and more important than any which has been claimed for or by her in the past.

While she will be conceded full political and

social rights on an equality with men, she will be placed in a position of responsibility and power which will render her his superior, since the future moral progress of the race will so largely depend upon her free choice in marriage.   As time goes on, and she acquires more and more economic independence, *that* alone will give her an effective choice which she has never had before.   But this choice will be further strengthened by the fact that, with ever-increasing approach to equality of opportunity for every child born in our country, that terrible excess of male deaths, in boyhood and early manhood especially due to various preventable causes, will disappear, and change the present majority of women to a majority of men.   This will lead to a greater rivalry for wives, and will give to women the power of rejecting all the lower types of character among their suitors.

It will be their special duty so to mould public opinion, through home training and social influence, as to render the women of the future the regenerators of the entire human race.

In closing this review of a great life, we cannot refrain from reflecting on the pendulum of scientific opinion.   The discovery of a great truth such as the law of selection is always followed by an over-valuation, from which there is certain to be a reaction.   We are in the midst of such a reaction at the present time, in which the Darwin-Wallace theory of natural selection is less appreciated than it will be in the future when there comes a fresh readjustment of scientific values.

It is well to remember that we may not estimate either the man of science or his conclusions as of our own period, but must project ourselves in imagination into the beginnings of his thought and into the travails of his mind, considering how much larger he was than the men about him, how far he was an innovator, breaking away from the traditions of his times, how far his direct observations apart from theory are true and permanent, and how far his theories have contributed to the great stream of biological thought.

Our perspective has covered a long, honorable span of sixty-five years into the beginnings of the thinking life of a natural philosopher whose last volume, "The World of Life," of the year 1911, gives as clear a portrayal of his final opinions as that which his first essay of 1858 portrays of his early opinions.

We follow the cycle of his reflection beginning with "adaptation" as the great mystery to be solved; in the middle and sanguine period of life, "adaptation" is regarded as fully explained by natural selection; in the closing and conservative period of life "adaptation" is again regarded in some of its phases as entirely beyond human powers of interpretation, not only in the evolution of the mental and spiritual nature of man, but in such marvellous manifestations as the scales of butterflies or the wings of birds.

From our own intellectual experience we may sympathize with the rebound of maturity from the buoyant confidence of the young man of thirty-five who finds in natural selection the entire solution of the problem of fitness which has vexed the mind and aroused the scientific curiosity of man since the time of Empedocles. We have ourselves experienced a loss of confidence with advancing years, an increasing humility in the face of transformations which become more and more mysterious the more we study them, although we may not join with this master in his appeal to an organizing and directing supernatural principle. Younger men than Wallace, both among the zoologists and philosophers of our own time, are giving a somewhat similar metaphysical solution of the eternal problem of adaptation, which still baffles and transcends our powers of experiment and of reasoning.

Photographed by his son, Leonard Darwin

CHARLES DARWIN

CHARLES DARWIN
1809-1882

I met Darwin in Huxley's laboratory and my impression of his personality is described in the address on the Life and Works of Darwin, which was delivered at Columbia University on the hundredth anniversary of his birth, as an introduction to a series of nine lectures on Charles Darwin and his influence in science. The fact that Lincoln and Darwin were born on the same day, February 12, 1809, brought together these two great men, so widely different in their vocations, so similar in their reverence for the truth, in their simplicity and directness of life.

The address at the Darwin Centenary at Cambridge was delivered at the request of my American colleagues, in reply to the reception of the delegates. It was strictly limited as to time, presenting the problem of speaking of Darwin to the men who knew him personally, who recalled almost every detail of his life—to sum up in comparatively few words the outstanding facts of his influence. The form of this address is therefore quite in contrast to the preceding tribute, which was without time limitation.

LIFE AND WORKS OF DARWIN

I

COLUMBIA UNIVERSITY is celebrating the hundredth anniversary of the birth of Darwin, the fiftieth anniversary of the publication of the "Origin of Species." In the year 1809 many illustrious men[1] were born, among them Darwin and Lincoln, one hundred years ago today, February 12. So widely different in their lives, Darwin and Lincoln were yet alike in simplicity of character and of language, in love of truth, in abhorrence of slavery, and especially in unconsciousness of their power. Both were at a loss to understand their influence over other men. "I am nothing and truth is everything," once wrote Lincoln. In concluding his autobiography Darwin wrote:

With such moderate abilities as I possess, it is truly surprising that I should have influenced to a considerable extent the belief of scientific men on some important points. My success as a man of science has been determined as far as I can judge, by complex and diversified mental qualities and

[1] Alfred Tennyson, Edgar Allen Poe, Felix Mendelssohn, Oliver Wendell Holmes, William Ewart Gladstone.

conditions. Of these, the most important have been the love of science, unbounded patience in long reflecting over any subject, industry in observing and collecting facts, a fair share of invention as well as of common sense.

Lincoln's greatest single act was his death-blow to slavery. Man had been fighting for centuries for freedom, in labor, in government, in religion, and in mind. It is certainly notable that the final victory for bodily liberty was won during the very years which witnessed the final emancipation of the mind. I do not see that Darwin's supreme service to his fellow men was his demonstration of evolution—man could have lived on quite as happily and perhaps more morally under the old notion that he was specially made in the image of his Maker. Darwin's supreme service was that he won for man absolute freedom in the study of the laws of nature; he literally fulfilled the saying of St. John, "Ye shall know the truth, and the truth shall make you free."

When we look back upon the very recent years of 1858–59, the years of revolution, we see that we were far from free either to study nature or reason about it. Our intellectual

chains were from the forges of theology both
catholic and protestant. The Bible was read
as a revelation of physical law rather than as
an epic of righteousness and spiritual law.
Theology while in power was itself in a most
critical position, in a *cul-de-sac* of antagonism
to reason and common sense, and this despite
the warnings of Augustine and of Bacon. As
early as the fifth century the wise theologian
of Numidia had said:

Leave questions of the earth and the sky and
the other elements of this world to reasoning and
observation. Perceiving that you are as far from
the truth as the east from the west the man of
science will scarce restrain his laughter.

Similarly, the great founder of the inductive
method observed:

Do not excite the laughter of men of science
through an absurd mixture of matters human and
divine. Do not commit the consummate folly
of building a system of natural philosophy on the
first chapter of Genesis or on the Book of Job.

It is difficult for the college student in this
day of liberty, if not of license, to realize that,
in the words of Lowell:

We breathe cheaply in the common air thoughts
that great hearts once broke for.

When, in 1844, Darwin communicated to the botanist Hooker under promise of secrecy his outline of evolution, he well knew the opprobrium it would bring, for he subsequently added (1846):

When my notes are published I shall fall infinitely low in the opinion of all *sound* naturalists, so this is my prospect for the future.

From the borders of Poland in 1543, or just three centuries earlier, Copernicus had published his "Revolutions of the Heavenly Bodies" and thus fired the first shot in a three hundred years' war for freedom to observe nature. In 1611 the telescope of Galileo demonstrated the truth of the Copernican law that the earth moves around the sun; and the most impressive object today in Florence is the model of the finger of this great astronomer as he held it up before the examiners of the Inquisition, with the words, "It still moves."

As time advanced the prison gave way to the milder but effective weapons of ostracism and loss of position. In biology Linnæus, Buffon, Lamarck, St. Hilaire, in turn discovered the evidences of evolution, but felt

the penalty and either recanted or suffered
loss of position. The cause of supernatural-
ism had never seemed stronger than in 1857;
the masterly works of Paley and Whewell
had appeared; the great series of Bridgewater
Treatises to demonstrate the wisdom and
goodness of God in the special creation of
adaptations had just been closed; men of
rare ability, Cuvier, Owen, Lyell and Agassiz,
were on the side of special creation; yet at
the very time this whole system of natural
philosophy was rotten at the foundation because it was not the work of free observation.

Where his great predecessors Buffon and
Lamarck had failed, Darwin won through his
unparalleled genius as an observer and rea-
soner, through the absolutely irresistible force
of the facts he had assembled and through
the simplicity of his presentation. Lacking
the literary graces of his grandfather, Erasmus Darwin, and the obscurity of Spencer,
Darwin was understood by every one as every
one could understand Lincoln. It is true the
cause was immediately championed by able
men, but victory was gained not by the vehe-
ment and radical Haeckel nor yet by the masterly fighter Huxley, but through the resist-

less power of the truth as Darwin saw it and presented it. It was not a denial, as had been the great sceptical movement of the end of the eighteenth century, but an affirmation. Darwin was not destroying but building; yet at the time good and honest men trembled as if passing through an earthquake, for in the whole history of human thought there had been no such cataclysm.

II

In what he achieved Darwin is so entirely alone that his place in the history of ideas is next to Aristotle, the great Greek biologist and philosopher who preceded him by over two thousand years.

The biographers of Lincoln are at a loss to explain his greatness through heredity. Darwin belonged to an able family, and his ancestors are singularly prophetic of his career. He was near of kin to Francis Galton, who shares with Weismann the leadership in the study of heredity during the nineteenth century. By a happy combination of all the best traits of the best of his ancestors coupled with the no less happy omission of other traits, Darwin was a far greater man than any of his forebears. Kindliness, truthfulness and love of nature were part of his birthright. From his grandfather Erasmus, Charles may have inherited especially his vividness of imagination and his strong tendency to generalize. Countless hypotheses flitted through his mind. "Without speculation there is no good and original observation," he wrote to Wallace. Still more interesting is the fact that the inheritance of his grandfather's tendency toward speculation took the direction of evolution, for before the close of the eighteenth century Erasmus Darwin gave the world in poetical form his belief in a complete evolutionary system as well as the first clear exposition of what is now known as the Lamarckian hypothesis. But in the grandson hypotheses were constantly held in check by the determination to put each to the severe test of observation. Darwin speaks of his father, Robert, as the most acute observer he ever saw, and attributes to him his intense desire to understand the reasons of things; from him came caution and conservatism. He says in his "Autobiography":

I have steadily endeavored to keep my mind free so as to give up any hypothesis (however much beloved), and I cannot resist forming one on every subject, as soon as facts are shown to be opposed to it.

If the "poet is born not made," the man of science is surely both born and made. Rare as was Darwin's genius, it was not more rare than the wonderful succession of outward events which shaped his life. It is true that Darwin believed with his cousin Francis Galton that education and environment produce only a small effect upon the mind of any one, but Darwin underestimated the force of his educational advantages just as he underestimated his own powers, and this because he thought only of his book and classroom life at school, at Edinburgh and at Cambridge, and not of his broader life. It was true in 1817, as today, that few teachers teach and few educators educate. It is true that those were the dull days of classical and mathematical drill. Yet look at the roster of Cambridge and see the men it produced. From Darwin's regular college work he may have gained but little, yet he was all the while enjoying an exceptional training. Step by step he was made a strong man by a mental guidance which is without parallel, by the precepts and example

of his father, for whom he held the greatest
reverence, by his reading of the poetry of
Shakespeare, Wordsworth, Coleridge and Milton, and the scientific prose of Paley, Herschel
and Humboldt, by the subtle scholarly influences of old Cambridge, by the scientific inspiration and advice of Henslow, by the mas-
terful inductive influence of the geologist
Lyell, and by the great nature panorama of
the voyage of the *Beagle.*

The college mates of Darwin saw more
truly than he himself what the old university
was doing for him. Professor Poulton of
Oxford believes that the kind of life which so
favored Darwin's mind has largely disap-
peared in English universities, especially under the sharp system of competitive examina-
tions; yet this is still more truly the atmosphere of old Cambridge today than of any of
our American colleges. It would be an interesting subject to debate whether we could
nurture such a man; whether a Darwin, were
he entered at a Columbia, a Harvard, a
Princeton, could develop mentally as Charles
Darwin did at Cambridge in 1828. I believe
that conditions for the favorable nurture of
such a mind are not with us. They are re-

pose, time for continuous thought, respect for
the man of brains and of individuality and of
such peculiar tastes as Darwin displayed in
his avidity for collecting beetles, freedom from
mental convention, general sympathy for nature, and, above all, ardor in the world of ideas.
If the genial mind cannot find the kindred
mind it cannot develop. Many American
school and college men are laughed out of the
finest promptings of their natures. In short,
I believe our intellectual environment would
be distinctly against a young Darwin today.

Thus event after event in Darwin's life was
singularly propitious. None but a Darwin
would have reflected these events as he did,
but grand and rare they certainly were.

At the age of nineteen he entered Christ's
of Cambridge, the small college which two
hundred years before had sheltered John Milton, the great poet of "Paradise Lost," the
epic of the special creation theory which it
was Darwin's destiny to destroy. His passion for sport, shooting, hunting, cross-coun-
try riding, his genial enjoyment of friends of
his own age, did not prevent delightful excursions with older men. He was known as
"the man who walks with Henslow"; and

close personal intercourse with this learned and genial botanist (Reverend Wm. C. Henslow) affected him more than any other feature of his college life. After graduation this personal association extended through Henslow to the geologist Sedgwick, who prepared him for the next step in his career. It was Henslow who secured for him his place on the exploring ship *Beagle* and the voyage round the world (1831–1836), by far the most important experience in his life.

No graduate course in any university can compare for a moment with the glorious vision which passed before young Darwin on the *Beagle*, but here again fortune smiled upon him, for this vision required the very scientific spirit and point of view which came to him through the reading of the "Principles of Geology" of Lyell, the masterly teacher of the uniformitarian doctrine of Hutton. That nature worked slowly in past as in present time and that the interpretation of the past is through observation of the present gave the note of Darwin's larger and more original interpretation, because the slow evolution which Lyell piously restricted to geology and the surface of the earth Darwin extended to biology and all living beings. If during the voyage Lyell's arguments convinced Darwin of the permanence of species, Lyell's way of looking at nature also gave him the means of seeing that species are not permanent. In his own words, he "saw through Lyell's eyes," and with the admiration of others always so characteristic of him his tribute to Lyell is without reserve. The second edition of "The Journal" is dedicated:

> With grateful pleasure as an acknowledgment that the chief part of whatever scientific merit this Journal and the other works of the author may possess has been derived from studying the well known and admirable "Principles of Geology."

The five years of the voyage filled the twenty-second to twenty-seventh years of Darwin's life, the period now ordinarily given to professional studies. In reading the simple but fascinating "Journal," which stands quite by itself in literature, we see how Darwin through his own genius and through the methods successively impressed upon him by his father, by Henslow, by Sedgwick and by Lyell was unconsciously preparing his mind for the "Origin of Species" and the "Descent of Man," the two most influential books of science which have ever appeared. From the islands of the Atlantic and the Pacific we follow his delightful comments on animals and plants of all kinds on sea and land, through forests, pampas and steppes, up the dry slopes of the Andes, along the salt lakes and deserts of Chili and of Australia. The dense forests of Brazil, pendant with orchids and gay with butterflies, contrast with those of Terra del Fuego and of Tahiti, and with the deforested Cape de Verde Islands. On these islands, the first he visits, he is enormously impressed by the superiority of Lyell's method. He visits other islands of all kinds, inhabited and uninhabited, the non-volcanic St. Paul's rocks, half-submerged volcanic cones, coral reefs and islands of the south Pacific. He observes live glaciers, as well as the contrasting action of active and of dead volcanoes. Along the rivers of Patagonia he unearths great extinct or fossil mammals; in Peru he studies the extinct races of man; the aborigines of Terra del Fuego and of Patagonia make the most profound impression upon his mind. In brief, he sees the great drama of nature in all its lesser scenes and in all its grander acts. He begins the voyage a firm believer in the fixity of species, but doubts begin to enter his mind when in the sands of the pampas of South America he perceives that the extinct forms are partly ancestral to the living, and when on the isolated Galapagos Islands he finds the life is not that of a special creation but that detached from the continent of South America six hundred miles distant.

Darwin says:

I owe to the voyage the first real training and education of my mind. That my mind had developed is rendered probable by my father's first exclamation on my return, "why the shape of his head is quite altered."

III

Soon after Darwin's return he moved to London for the two most active years of his life, to care for his collections and to write up his observations. At this moment came the third of the great turning-points in his life, which as a mysteriously disguised blessing was brought about through ill health. In London he was entering official duties and public scientific service which would undoubtedly have increased and interfered more and more seriously with his work. We can only count

it as one of the most fortunate circumstances
in the history of science that Darwin at the
age of thirty-three was forced to leave London and to move to Down. Here for forty
years he never knew for one day the health of
an ordinary man; his life was one long struggle against the strain of sickness. But unreal-
ized by him there was the compensation of a
mind undisturbed by the constant interruption of outside affairs, such interruption as
killed Huxley and is killing so many fine and
ambitious men today. When I saw Huxley
and Darwin side by side in 1879, the one only
fifty-four, the other seventy, the younger man
looked by far the more careworn of the two.
Huxley, the strong man, broke down mentally
at fifty-six; Darwin, the invalid, was vigorous mentally at seventy-two.

Darwin's writings fall into three grand
series. In the nine years after he returned
from the voyage, or between his twenty-
seventh and thirty-sixth years, Darwin wrote
the first series, including his pre-evolutionary
geological and zoological works, his "Coral
Reefs" (1842), his "Zoology and Geology of
the Voyage of the *Beagle*" (1844–1846), his
"Journal of Researches," the popular narra-

tive of his voyage (1845). Darwin's ill health thereafter shut him off from geology, although his last volume, "The Earthworm," was in a sense geological.

It is characteristic of the life of every great man that his genius and his own self-analysis instinctively guide him to discover his mental needs.

Until the age of forty-five Darwin in his own opinion had not completed his education, in the sense that education is a broad and exact training. He now proceeded to fill the one gap in his training by devoting the eight years of his life between thirty-seven and forty-five to a most laborious research upon the barnacles, or Cirripedia. This gave him the key to the principles of the natural or adaptively branching and divergent arrangement of animals through the laws of descent as set forth in the "Origin," which he certainly could not have secured in any other way. The value he placed on his work on the barnacles is of especial import today when systematic work is so lightly esteemed by many biologists, young and old. Darwin subsequently, in the words of Hooker, "recognized three stages in his career as a biologist, the mere collector at Cambridge, the collector and observer on the *Beagle* and for some years afterwards, and the trained naturalist after, and only after, the Cirripede work."

Long before this, however, at the age of twenty-eight, Darwin had begun his career as a Darwinian. In July, 1837, he began his notes on the transmutation of species, based on purely Baconian principles, on the rigid collection of facts which would bear in any way on the variations of animals and plants under domestication and in nature. Rare as was his reasoning power, his powers of observation were of a still more distinct order. He persistently and doggedly followed every clew; he noticed little things which escaped others; he always noted exceptions and at once jotted down facts opposed to his theories. On the voyage the marvellous adaptations of animals and plants had been his greatest puzzle. Fifteen months later, in October, 1838, in reading the work of Malthus, on "Population," there flashed across his mind the threefold clew of the struggle for existence, of constant variability, and of the selection of variations which happen to be adaptive.

The three memorable features of Darwin's

greatest work, "The Origin of Species," are, that he was twenty-one years in preparing it, that, although by 1844 he was a strongly convinced evolutionist and natural selectionist, he kept on with his observations for fifteen years, and the volume even then would have been still longer postponed but for a wonderful coincidence, which constitutes the third and not the least memorable feature. This coincidence was that Wallace had also become an evolutionist and had also discovered the principle of natural selection through the reading of the same essay of Malthus. It is further remarkable that of all persons Wallace selected Darwin as the one to whom to send his paper. It was then through the persuasion of the great botanist Hooker, who had known Darwin's views for thirteen years, that these independent discoveries were published jointly on July 1, 1858. All the finest points of Darwin's personal character were displayed at this time; in fact, the entire Darwin-Wallace history up to and including Wallace's noble and self-depreciatory tribute to Darwin on July 1 of last summer, is one of the brightest chapters in the history of science. Wallace himself pointed out the very important distinction that while the theories contained in the two papers published fifty years ago were nearly identical, Wallace had deliberated only three days after coming across the passage in Malthus, while Darwin had deliberated for fifteen years. He modestly declared that the respective credit should be in the ratio of fifteen years to three days.

Several months past the age of fifty Darwin published his epoch-making work (November, 1859), and despite ill health, between fifty and seventy-three he produced the nine great volumes which expand and illustrate the views expressed in "The Origin of Species."

A parallel to this remarkable late productiveness is that of Kant, who also put forth his greatest work after fifty. Let those past the five decades take heart, for it appears that while there are inborn differences between men in this regard, imagination, observation, reasoning and production do not necessarily dim with age. Darwin's mind remained young and plastic to the end; his latest and one of his most characteristic works, "The Formation of Vegetable Mould through the Action of Earth Worms," was published at the age of seventy-two, after forty-four years

of observation. It contained another and
perhaps the most extreme demonstration of
Lyell's principle that vast changes in nature
are brought about by the slow operation of
infinitesimal causes.

Three of Darwin's succeeding volumes are
a filling out of the "Origin." "The Variation
of Animals and Plants under Domestication"
(two volumes, 1868) presents the entire fabric
of the notes begun twenty-one years before on
the transmutation of species. "The Descent
of Man" (1871) was another logical outcome
of the "Origin," yet it was only faintly adum-
brated by a single allusion in that work to
the fact that the transmutation of species
necessarily led to the evolution of man. The
"Descent" marks the third of the great dates
in the history of thought, as the "Origin"
marks the second, because it is the final step
in the development of ideas which began
with Copernicus in 1543. The world-wide
sensation, the mighty *storm* produced by this
bold climax of Darwin's work, is so fresh in
the memory of all that a mere allusion suffices.
The evolutionary or genetic basis for modern
psychology as stated in "The Descent of
Man" was given still more concrete form in

Darwin's succeeding and most delightful volume, "The Expression of the Emotions" (1872).

The knowledge of zoology and anatomy displayed in these four evolutionary volumes came from direct observation, vast and systematic reading and note-taking from the simple materials which Darwin could collect at Down. Always penetrating as these observations are, they are still, in my opinion, surpassed in beauty and ingenuity by his marvellous work on plants, published between 1862 and 1880. Here the principles of co-adaptation of plants and insects in cross- and self-fertilization, in climbing plants and insectivorous plants, in forms of flowers, in movements of plants, are all brought forth in support of the theory of natural selection and the operation of unknown laws. Darwin's most precise observations and some of his most brilliant discoveries recorded in these volumes laid the foundations of modern experimental botany.

Of his method Darwin writes:

From my early youth I had the strongest desire to understand or explain whatever I observed, that is, to group facts under some general laws.

My mind seems to have become a kind of machine for grinding general laws out of large collections of facts.

The only work which Darwin wrote deductively was his "Coral Reefs." Every other volume came through the inductive-deductive process, that is, through an early assemblage of facts followed by a series of trial hypotheses, each of which was rigidly tested by additional facts. The most central of these trial hypotheses was that of the building up of adaptations through the selection of the single adaptive variation out of the many fortuitous variations, and this Darwin was unable to rigidly test by facts but was obliged to leave for verification or disproof by work after him.

IV

On December 8, 1879, when Darwin was in his seventieth year and I in my twenty-second, I had the rare privilege of meeting him and looking steadily in his face during a few moments' conversation. It was in Huxley's laboratory, and I was at the time working upon the anatomy of the Crustacea. The entry in my journal is as follows:

This is a red letter day for me. As I was leaning over my lobster (*Homarus vulgaris*) this morning, cutting away at the brain, I raised my head and looked up to see Huxley and Darwin passing by me. I believe I never shall see two such great naturalists together again. I went on apparently with skill, really hacking my brain away, and cast an occasional glance at the great old gray-haired man. I was startled, so unexpected was it, by Huxley speaking to me and introducing me to Darwin as "an American who has already done some good palæontological work on the other side of the water." I gave Darwin's hand a tremendous squeeze (for I never shall shake it again) and said, without intending, in an almost reverential tone, "I am very glad to meet you." He stands much taller than Huxley, has a very ruddy face, with benevolent blue eyes and overhanging eyebrows. His beard is quite long and perfectly white and his hair falls partly over a low forehead. His features are not good. My general impression of his face is very pleasant. He smiled broadly, said something about a hope that Marsh with his students would not be hindered in his work, and Huxley, saying "I must not let you talk too much," hurried him on into the next room.

I may add, as distinctly recorded in my memory, that the impression of Darwin's bluish-gray eyes, deep-set under the overhanging brows, was that they were the eyes of a man who could survey all nature.

Another memory of interest is that the instant Huxley closed the door I was mobbed as the "lucky American" by the ninety less fortunate students of Great Britain and other countries.

Huxley's solicitude for Darwin's strength was characteristic of him. He often alluded to himself as "Darwin's bull dog."

I have already stated that of the two men Darwin gave the impression of enjoying the better health. Huxley was then sixteen years the younger, yet the burdens and strain of London life made him look less young and hale. In this connection an earlier jotting from the same laboratory is as follows:

Huxley comes in as the clock strikes and begins to lecture at once, almost before it ceases. He looks old and somewhat broken, his eyes deeply sunken, but is a lecturer as strong as he ever could have been. His language is very simple too.

V

Darwin passed away in the year 1882, at the age of seventy-three. Out of the simple and quiet life at Down he had sent forth the great upheaval and revolution.

On this centenary when we are honoring

Darwin, many may ask, exactly what is Darwinism? Failure to know leads some to doubt, others to predict a decline, especially where "the wish is father to the thought." Nothing could be less true than to say that there is the least abatement in the force of the main teaching of this great leader, namely, of the evolutionary law of the universe. The vitality of this idea is shown by its invasion of the physical world. Again, Darwinism is the sum of Darwin's observations on earth structure, on plants, animals and man. This vast body of truth and of interpretation still so far surpasses that brought forward by any other observer of nature, and these facts and interpretations are so far confirmed that they have become the very foundation-stones of modern biology and geology. Finally, looking at Darwinism as the sum of his generalizations as to the processes of evolution we again find a vast body of well-established laws which are also daily becoming more evident. As to the laws of evolution, there is no single biological principle more absolutely proved by the study of living and extinct things since Darwin's time than the broad law of natural selection: certainly the fittest survive and reproduce their kind, the fittest of every degree, all classes, orders, genera, species, individuals and even the fittest organs and fittest separate parts of organs. Darwin still gives us the only explanation which has ever been suggested of hundreds of thousands of adaptations of which neither Buffon's view of direct effect of environment nor Lamarck's view of the inheritance of bodily modifications even approaches an explanation worthy to be considered. Take the egg of the murre or guillemot, which is so much larger at one end than the other that it cannot roll off the cliff on which it is laid, or the seasonal changes of color in the ptarmigan, every one of which is protective.

There is some lack of perspective, some egotism, much one-sidedness in modern criticism. The very announcement, "Darwin deposed," attracts such attention as would the notice "Mt. Blanc removed"; does it not bespeak courage to attack a lion even when deceased? Preoccupation in the study of one great law, as in the case of Bateson on Mendelism and De Vries on Mutation, blinds to every other law. To be dispassionate, let us remember that Darwin's hypothesis was framed in 1838,

seventy-one years ago. Are the two great
Cambridge men, Newton and Darwin, lesser
men because astronomy and biology are progressive sciences? Secondly, to know your
Darwin you must not judge him by single passages but by all he wrote. Darwin is not to
be known through the extremes of those of his
followers with whom an hypothesis has become
a creed. Reading him afresh and through and
through we discover that his "variation" and
"variability" are very broad and elastic
terms. Every actual example he cites of his
main hypothesis, such as the speed of the
wolf or the deer, or the long neck of the
giraffe, is a variation both heritable and of
adaptive value.

When we put together all the concrete cases
which he gave to illustrate his views of selection we see that he includes both continuous
and discontinuous variations, both the shades
of difference of kind and proportion and the
little leaps or saltations from character to
character. For example, certain cases of immunity to disease are now known to be "unit
characters" in Bateson's sense, or "mutants"
in the De Vries sense. Darwin repeatedly
referred to immunity as a variation which

would be preserved by selection. Moreover, Darwin's own repeated assertion of his profound ignorance of the laws of variation certainly pointed the way to the investigation of these laws, and it is this very study which is modifying the applications of his selection hypothesis.

From first to last Huxley maintained that it would require many years of study before naturalists could say whether Darwin had been led to overestimate the power of natural selection. Darwin's mind from first to last was also open on this point. Through every edition of the "Origin" we find the passage:

The laws governing the incipient or primordial variations (unimportant except as the groundwork for selection to act on and then all important) I shall discuss under several heads. But I can come, as you may well believe, to only very partial and imperfect conclusions.

In 1869 and in the latest edition of the "Origin" Darwin speaks of "individual differences" as of paramount importance, but he illustrates these differences by such instances as the selection of passenger pigeons with more powerful wings, or the selection of the lightest colored birds in deserts.

There can be no question, however, that
Darwin did love his selection theory and
somewhat overestimated its importance. His
conception of selection in nature may be compared to a series of concentric circles constantly narrowing from the largest groups
down to the minutest structures. In the
operations of this intimate circle of minute
variations within organisms he was inclined
to believe two things: first, that the fit or
adaptive always arises out of the accidental,
or that out of large and minute variations
without direction selection brings direction and
fitness; second, as a consistent pupil of Lyell,
he was inclined to believe that the chief
changes in evolution are slow and continuous.

The psychology of Darwin was in a reaction state from the prevailing false teleology;
he was not expecting that purposive or teleo-
logical or even orthogenetic laws of variation
would be discovered. William James has
thus recently expressed and endorsed the
spirit of Darwinism as a new natural philosophy in the following words:

It is strange, considering how unanimously our
ancestors felt the force of this argument [that is,
the teleological], to see how little it counts for

since the triumph of the Darwinian theory. Darwin opened our minds to the power of the chance-happenings to bring forth "fit" results if only they have time to add themselves together. He showed the enormous waste of nature in producing results that get destroyed because of their unfitness.

The question before us naturalists today is whether this non-teleological spirit of Darwinism as expressed by William James corresponds with the actual order of evolution in nature. This really involves the deep-seated query whether the intimate or minute parts of living things are operating under natural laws like non-living things or are really lawless.

Before expressing my individual opinion based on my own researches of the last twenty years I may summarize the general modern dissent: in *three points* it may be said that Darwin's teachings are not accepted today.

First, his slowly developed belief in the inheritance of bodily modifications and the provisional "assemblage theory" of heredity which he called *pangenesis* has been set aside for Weismann's law that heredity lies in the continuity of a specific heredity plasm, and for want of evidence of the transmission of acquired characters.

Second, while his prevailing belief that

changes in organisms are in the main slow
and continuous is now positively demonstrated
to be correct by the study of descent in fossil
organisms, there is also positive evidence for
the belief which he less strongly entertained
that many changes are discontinuous or mu-
tative, as held by Bateson and De Vries.

Finally, his belief that out of fortuitous
or undirected variations in minute characters arise direction, purpose and adaptation
through selection still lacks proof by either
observation or experiment. Fossil and other
descent series entirely unknown in Darwin's
time prove beyond question that law rather
than chance is prevailing in variation.

What the nature of these laws is it is still
too early to say. Personally I am strongly of
the opinion that the laws of life, like the ulti-
mate laws of physics, may eventually prove to
be beyond analysis.

To allow myself just one flight of fanciful
statement drawn from personal observation
and reflection I may say there is a likeness
between the unit forces working in a single
organism, both as revealed by the microscope
and in fossil series, and the individual soldiers
composing a giant army. The millions of

well-ordered activities in the body correspond with the millions of intelligently trained men who compose the army; the selection process or the survival of the fittest is like the competition between two armies, between the Russian and Japanese, for example. It is an outward and visible competition between two internally prepared and well-ordered hosts of units and groups of units. Selection is continuously working upon the army as a whole and also upon every unit which affects survival—an immunity unit, an intelligence unit, a speed unit, a color or group of color units; just as in the army it is working upon units of courage, of strategy, of precision of fire, of endurance, of mass. In this sense it is perfectly true to say with Darwin "that selection works upon certain single variations." It is not true, or at least it is not shown, that these variations are a matter of chance; they rather appear to be a matter of law, as indeed Darwin foresaw when he stated that he used the word "chance" merely as a synonym of "ignorance."

In the present state of biology we are studying the behavior of the thousands of parts, sometimes of blending, sometimes of separate, sometimes of paired or triplicate units, which compose the whole and make up the individual organism. Natural selection determines which organism shall win; more than this, it determines which serviceable activities of each organism shall win. Here lie the limits of its power. Selection is not a creative but a judicial principle. It is one of Darwin's many triumphs that he positively demonstrated that this judicial principle is one of the great factors of evolution. Then he clearly set our task before us in pointing out that the *unknown* lies in the laws of variation, and a stupendous task it is. At the same time he left us a legacy in his inductive and experimental methods by which we may blaze our trail.

Therefore, in this anniversary year, we do not see any decline in the force of Darwinism but rather a renewed stimulus to progressive search. As Huxley says:

But this one thing is perfectly certain—that is, it is only by pursuing his method, by that wonderful single-mindedness, devotion to truth, readiness to sacrifice all things for the advance of definite knowledge, that we can hope to come any nearer than we are at present to the truths which he struggled to attain.

THE DARWIN CENTENARY AT CAMBRIDGE

CROSSING the Atlantic in honor of Darwin and rejoicing in the privilege of uniting in this celebration of his birth, we desire, first of all, to render our tribute to the University of Cambridge. . . .

What can we add to the chorus of appreciation of the great pupil of Christ's which has come from college, press and pulpit since the opening of this anniversary year? Only a few words of *personal impression*.

To us, Darwin, more perhaps than any other naturalist, seems greatest in the union of a high order of genius with rare simplicity and transparency of thought. Dwelling on this lucid quality and on the vast range of his observation from the most minute to the grandest relations in nature, does not the image arise of a perfected optical instrument in which all personal equation, aberration and refraction are eliminated and through which, as it were, we gaze with a new vision into the marvellous forms and processes of the living world? With this wondrous lens our countrymen, Cope and Marsh, penetrated far deeper into fossil life than their predecessor Joseph Leidy, and the arid deserts of the Rocky Mountain region gave up their petrified dead as proofs of Darwinism. Through its new powers Hyatt, Morse, Packard and Brooks saw far more than their master Louis Agassiz and drew fresh testimonies of development from the historic waters of New England. From the very end of the new world, where the youthful Darwin received his first impressions of the mutability of the forms of life, we enjoy a clearer vision of the ancient life of Patagonia.

What of Darwin's future influence?

While it is doubtful if human speculation about life can ever again be so tangential as in our pre-Darwinian past of fifty years ago, it is probable, in fact it is daily becoming more evident, that the destiny of speculation is less the tangent than the maze—the maze of innumerable lesser principles, with as many prophets calling to us to seek this turning or that. There are those who in loyal advocacy of his system feel that we shall not get much nearer to life than Darwin did, but this is to abandon his progressive leadership, for if ever a master defined the unknown and pointed the way of investigation, certainly it was Darwin. In the wonderful round of addresses in his honor of this Centennial Year and in the renewed critical study of his life and writings, the recognition that Darwin opened the way has come to many with the force of a fresh discovery. It is true that he left a system and that he loved it as his own, but his forceful, self-unsparing and suggestive criticism show that if he were living in these days of Waagen, of Weismann, of Mendel and of De Vries, he would be in the front line of inquiry, armed with matchless assemblage of fact, with experiment and verification, and not least with incomparable candor and good will. This bequest of a noble method is hardly less precious than the immortal content of the "Origin of Species" itself.

From a photograph copyright by Elliott and Fry

THOMAS HENRY HUXLEY

THOMAS HENRY HUXLEY
1825–1895

To the memory of Balfour and of Huxley, my chief teacher in comparative anatomy, I dedicated my work, "The Age of Mammals." Huxley set forth the logic of Darwin as applied to palæontology. Only a few men of the last century had the gift of speaking in clear language both to the learned and unlearned, and the greatest of these was Huxley. To write both for the man of one's own profession and for the layman, to be accurate and abreast of the specialist who knows a subject as well as or better than you do, while intelligible to the non-specialist—there is the difficulty. Many times have I thought how simple it would be to address either audience separately. Yet I consider it fortunate that both are with us, because I share Huxley's confidence in addressing those who are willing to do a little serious thinking in order to enjoy the vast vistas of interesting truth which come as the reward of effort. I share also his conviction that it is the duty of the man of science to devote a certain part of his time, however absorbed in research he may be, to an honest attempt to scatter scientific truth.

During the winter of 1879–80 I attended Huxley's full course of lectures on Comparative Anatomy and Evolution, which were delivered in the upper floor of the Royal College of Science. In "A Student's Reminiscences of Huxley" I especially attempt to describe personal impressions which he made upon me as a lecturer and as a thinker and to record some of the flashes of wit with which he enlivened his lectures. Although intensely occupied at the time with a variety of public education matters and with the pressure of literary and scientific work, Huxley found time, chiefly in his home, to enter into conversation on the subjects flooding his mind. It was there that I heard some of the best stories here recorded.

A STUDENT'S REMINISCENCES OF HUXLEY

BY far the larger number of American students who go abroad pass through the English Channel, obtain a distant view of the mother country and, after from one to three years in Germany, return with an exclusively German education. Neither England nor France having been visited, the implication is that the countries which produced Owen, Darwin, Huxley and Balfour, or Lamarck, Cuvier, St. Hilaire and Pasteur have nothing to offer the American student. This is not the fact; the fact is that England and France are a half-century behind Germany in that kind of university organization which attracts a foreign student and enables him immediately to find his level and enter upon his research. English and French universities until a very recent date either have been not so fully prepared or have met the newcomer with practically insuperable obstacles in the matter of a degree.

None the less, the student who has not breasted these obstacles for the compensating

advantages which the English and French
schools offer has made a serious mistake. He
has brought back not an Old World education, but an exclusively German education,
with its splendidly sound and unique features
and with many inherent defects. Germany
produces the generals and the rank and file of
the armies of science, but certainly the com-
manders-in-chief, in biology at least, have
been Englishmen. If we find the highest
exponents of purely inductive research in
Germany, we certainly find a better union of
the inductive and deductive methods in
France and England. France leads in expression and style of thought, although, upon
the whole, less sound in substance than Germany. England and France in her best
period have given us the most far-reaching
and permanent generalizations in biology. It
follows that the American student who can
afford the experience will profit most by plac-
ing himself successively in the scientific atmosphere of Germany, France, and England.
My own post-graduate education was unfor-
tunately not of this three-sided type. None
the less, it has always seemed a most fortunate circumstance that in the spring of 1879

a letter from the venerable Kitchen Parker led me to Cambridge and to the great privilege of sitting under Balfour, the most brilliant and lovable of men. In the following autumn Huxley's lectures upon Comparative Zoology began in October, and by entering this course I came to know personally this great master and through him to enjoy the rare opportunity of meeting Charles Darwin. After this experience, which was equally open to any serious student of biology at that time, it is natural that I should strongly advise those of you who are planning your foreign studies to spend part of your time in England and endeavor to discern some of the distinctive qualities of English men of science which Huxley so nobly illustrated. You will pardon the personal element in the following recollections of Huxley as a teacher and the rather informal review of his life-work.

Huxley as a teacher can never be forgotten by any of his students. He entered his lecture-room promptly as the clock was striking nine, rather quickly and with his head bent forward "as if oppressive with its mind." He usually glanced attention to his class of about ninety and began speaking before he reached his chair. He spoke between his lips, with perfectly clear analysis, with thorough interest, and with philosophic insight which was far above the average of his students. He used very few charts, but handled the chalk with great skill, sketching out the anatomy of an animal as if it were a transparent object. As in Darwin's face, and as in Erasmus Darwin's, Buffon's, and many other anatomists with a strong sense of form, his eyes were heavily overhung by a projecting forehead and eyebrows and seemed at times to look inward. His lips were firm and closely set, with the expression of positiveness, and the other feature which most marked him was the very heavy mass of hair falling over his forehead, which he would frequently stroke or toss back. Occasionally he would lighten up the monotony of anatomical description by a bit of humor. I remember one instance which was probably reminiscent of his famous tilt with Bishop Wilberforce at the meeting of the British Association in 1860. Huxley was describing the mammalian heart and had just distinguished between the tricuspid valve, on the right side of the heart, and the bicuspid

valve, on the left, which you know resembles
a bishop's mitre, and hence is known as the
mitral valve.   He said:

It is not easy to recall on which side these
respective valves are found, but I recommend
this rule: you can easily remember that the mitral
is on the left, because a bishop is never known
to be on the right.

Huxley was the father of modern laboratory instruction, but in 1879 he was so intensely engrossed with his own researches
that he very seldom came through the laboratory, which was ably directed by T. Jeffrey Parker, assisted by G. B. Howes and W.
Newton Parker, all of whom are now professors, Howes having succeeded to Huxley's
chair.   Each visit therefore inspired a certain
amount of terror, which was really unwar-
ranted, for Huxley always spoke in the kind-
est tones to his students, although sometimes
he could not resist making fun at their expense.   There was an Irish student who sat
in front of me, whose anatomical drawings
in water-color were certainly most remarkable productions.   Huxley, in turning over
his drawing-book, paused at a large blur
under which was carefully inscribed "sheep's

liver" and smilingly said: "I am glad to know that is a liver; it reminds me as much of Cologne Cathedral in a fog as of anything I have ever seen before." Fortunately the nationality of the student enabled him to fully appreciate the humor.

The greatest event in the winter of 1879 was Darwin's first and only visit to the laboratory. They came in together, Huxley leading slowly down the long, narrow room, pointing out the especial methods of teaching, which he had originated and which are now universally adopted in England and in this country. Darwin was instantly recognized by the class as he entered and sent a thrill of curiosity down the room, for no one present had ever seen him before. There was the widest possible contrast in the two faces. Darwin's grayish-white hair and bushy eyebrows overshadowed a pair of deeply set blue eyes, which seemed to image his wonderfully calm and deep vision of nature and at the same time to emit benevolence. Huxley's piercing black eyes and determined and resolute face were full of admiration and, at the same time, protection of his older friend. He said afterward: "You know, I have to

take care of him; in fact, I have always
been Darwin's bulldog," and this exactly
expressed one of the many relations which
existed so long between the two men.

Huxley was not always fortunate in the
intellectual caliber of the men to whom he
lectured in the Royal College of Science. Many
of the younger generation were studying in
the universities, under Balfour at Cambridge
and under Rolleston at Oxford. However,
Saville Kent, C. Lloyd Morgan, George B.
Howes, T. Jeffrey Parker and W. Newton
Parker are representative biologists who were
directly trained by Huxley. Many others,
not his students, have expressed the deepest
indebtedness to him. Among these especially
are Professor E. Ray Lankester, of Oxford,
and Professor Michael Foster, of Cambridge.
Huxley once said that he had "discovered
Foster." He not only singled men out, but
knew how to direct and inspire them to inves-
tigate the most pressing problems of the day.
As it was, his thirty-one years of lectures
would have produced a far greater effect if
they had been delivered from an Oxford,
Cambridge or Edinburgh chair. In fact,
Huxley's whole life would have been different,

in some ways more effective, in others less so,
if the universities had welcomed the young
genius who was looking for a post and even
cast his eyes toward America in 1850, but in
those early days of classical prestige both
seats of learning were dead to the science
which it was Huxley's great service in support of Darwin to place beside physics in
the lead of all others in England. Moreover,
Oxford, if not Cambridge, could not long
have sheltered such a wolf in the fold.

Huxley's public addresses always gave the
impression of being largely impromptu, but
he once told me: "I always think out carefully every word I am going to say. There is
no greater danger than the so-called *inspiration of the moment*, which leads you to say
something which is not exactly true or which
you would regret afterward. I sometimes
envy your countrymen their readiness and
believe that a native American, if summoned
out of bed at midnight, could step to his
window and speak well upon any subject."
I told him I feared he had been slightly mis-
informed; I feared that many American impromptu speeches were distinguished more by
a flow of language than of ideas. But Hux-

ley was sometimes very impressive when he did not speak. In 1879 he was strongly advocating the removal of the Royal School of Mines from crowded Jermyn street to South Kensington, a matter which is still being agitated. At a public dinner given by the alumni of the school, who were naturally attached to the old buildings, the chairman was indiscreet enough to make an attack upon the policy of removal. He was vigorously applauded, when, to every one's consternation, Huxley, who was sitting at the chairman's right, slowly rose, paused a moment, and then silently skirted the tables and walked out of the hall. A solemn pall fell over us, which lasted throughout the dinner, and we were all glad to find an excuse to leave early.

In personal conversation Huxley was full of humor and greatly enjoyed stories at his own expense. Such was the following:

In my early period as a lecturer I had very little confidence in my general powers, but one thing I prided myself upon was clearness. I was once talking of the brain before a large mixed audience and soon began to feel that no one in the room understood me. Finally I saw the thoroughly interested face of a woman auditor and took consolation in delivering the remainder of the lecture directly to her. At the close, my feeling as to her interest was confirmed when she came up and asked if she might put one question upon a single point which she had not quite understood. "Certainly," I replied. "Now, Professor," she said, "is the cerebellum inside or outside of the skull?"

A story of his about babies is also characteristic:

When a fond mother calls upon me to admire her baby I never fail to respond, and, while cooing appropriately, I take advantage of an opportunity to gently ascertain whether the soles of its feet turn in and tend to support my theory of arboreal descent.

Huxley's life is as full of suggestion to the student as were his lectures and his conversation. It illustrates the force of obtaining a very broad view of the animal kingdom before we attempt to enter the plane of higher generalization. Huxley's training in embryology, vertebrate and invertebrate zoology, palæontology, and geology was not mapped out for him as for the modern university student. His prolonged sea voyage gave him time and material for reflection, and after this he was led from one subject to another until he obtained a grasp of nature as a whole second only to that of Darwin.

Huxley was born in 1825. Like Goethe, he inherited from his mother his brilliantly alert powers of thought, and from his father his courage and tenacity of purpose, a combination of qualities which especially fitted him for the period in which he was to live. There is nothing striking recorded about his boyhood as a naturalist. He preferred engineering but was led into medicine.

At the close of his medical course he secured a navy medical post upon the *Rattlesnake*. This brought with it, as to Darwin, the training of a four years' voyage to the South Seas off eastern Australia and west Guinea—a more liberal education to a naturalist than any university affords, even at the present day. This voyage began at twenty-one, and he says of it:

But, apart from experience of this kind and the opportunity afforded for scientific work, to me, personally, the cruise was extremely valuable. It was good for me to live under sharp discipline, to be down on the realities of existence by living on bare necessities, to find out how extremely worth living life seemed to be when one woke from a night's rest on a soft plank, with the sky

for a canopy and cocoa and weevily biscuit the
sole prospect for breakfast, and more especially
to learn to work for what I got for myself out of
it. My brother officers were as good as sailors
ought to be and generally are, but naturally they
neither knew nor cared anything about my pur-
suits, nor understood why I should be so zealous
in the pursuit of the objects which my friends,
the middies, christened "Buffons," after the title
conspicuous on a volume of the "Suites à Buffon,"
which stood in a prominent place on my shelf
in the chart room.

As the result of this voyage of four years
numerous papers were sent home to the Linnæan Society of London, but few were published; upon his return his first great work,
"Upon the Anatomy and Affinities of the
Medusæ," was declined for publication by
the Admiralty—a fortunate circumstance, for
it led to his quitting the navy for good and
trusting to his own resources. Upon publication, this memoir at once established his
scientific reputation at the early age of
twenty-four, just as Richard Owen had won
his spurs by his "Memoir on the Pearly Nau-
tilus." In 1852 Huxley's preference as a
biologist was to turn back to physiology,
which had become the favorite study of his

medical course.   But his fate was to enter
and become distinguished in a widely different branch, which had as little attraction for
him as for most students of marine life,
namely, palæontology.   He says of his sudden change of base:

At last, in 1854, on the translation of my warm
friend, Edward Forbes, to Edinburgh, Sir Henry
de la Beche, the Director-General of the Geological Survey, offered me the post Forbes had vacated
of Palæontologist and Lecturer on Natural History.   I refused the former point-blank, and accepted the latter only provisionally, telling Sir
Henry that I did not care for fossils and that I
should give up natural history as soon as I could
get a physiological post.   But I held the office
for thirty-one years, and a large part of my work
has been palæontological.

From this time until 1885 his labors extended over the widest field of biology and
of philosophy ever covered by any naturalist, with the single exception of Aristotle.
In philosophy Huxley showed rare critical
and historical power; he made the most exhaustive study of Hume, but his own philosophical spirit and temper were more directly
the offspring of Descartes.   Some subjects he
mastered, others he merely touched, but

every subject which he wrote about he illuminated. Huxley did not discover or first define protoplasm, but he made it known to the English-speaking world as the physical basis of life, recognizing the unity of animal and plant protoplasm. He cleared up certain problems among the Protozoa. In 1849 appeared his great work upon the oceanic Hydrozoa, and familiarity with these forms doubtless suggested the brilliant comparison of the two-layered gastrula to the adult Hydrozoa. He threw light upon the Tunicata, describing the endostyle as a universal feature, but not venturing to raise the Tunicata to a separate order. He set in order the cephalopod mollusca, deriving the spiral from the straight-shelled fossil forms. He contributed to the Arthropoda; his last word upon this group being his charming little volume upon the "Crayfish," a model of its kind. But think of the virgin field which opened up before him among the vertebrata, when in 1859 he was the first to perceive the truth of Darwin's theory of descent! Here were Cuvier's and Owen's vast researches upon living and extinct forms, a disorderly chaos of facts waiting for generalization.

Huxley was the man for the time. He had already secured a thoroughly philosophical basis for his comparative osteology by studying the new embryology of Von Baer, which Richard Owen had wholly ignored. In 1858 his famous Croonian lecture on the "Theory of the Vertebrate Skull" gave the death-blow to Owen's life-work upon the skull and vertebral archetype and to the whole system of mystical and transcendental anatomy; and now Huxley set to work vigorously to build out of Owen's scattered tribes the great limbs and branches of the vertebrate tree. He set the fishes and batrachia apart as the *Icthyopsidan* branch, the reptiles and birds as the *Sauropsidan* in contrast with the *Mammalian*, which he derived from a prosauropsidan or amphibian stem, a theory which with some modification has received strong recent verification.

Professor Owen, who had held undisputed sway in England up to 1858, fought nobly for opinions which had been idolized in the first half-century, but was routed at every point. Huxley captured his last fortress when, in his famous essay of 1865, "Man's Place in Nature," he undermined Owen's teaching of

the separate and distinct anatomical position
of man. We can only appreciate Huxley's
fighting qualities when we see how strongly
Owen was intrenched at the beginning of this
long battle royal; he was director of the
British Museum and occupied other high
posts; he had the strong moral support of
the government and of the royal family, although these were weak allies in a scientific
encounter.

Huxley's powers of rapid generalization, of
course, betrayed him frequently; his Bathyb-
ius was a groundless and short-lived hypothesis; he went far astray in the phylogeny of
the horses. But these and other errors were
far less attributable to defects in his reasoning powers than to the extraordinarily high
pressure under which he worked for the twenty years between 1860 and 1880, when duties
upon the Educational Board, upon the Government Fisheries Commission, and upon Par-
liamentary committees crowded upon him.
He had at his command none of the resources
of modern technique. He cut his own sections.
I remember once seeing some of his micro-
scopic sections. To one of our college junior
students working with a Minot microtome

Huxley's sections would have appeared like translucent beafsteaks—another illustration that it is not always the section which reveals the natural law, but the man who looks at the section.

Huxley was a master not only in the search for truth but in the way in which he presented it, both in writing and in speaking. And we are assured, largely as he was gifted by nature, his beautifully lucid and interesting style was partly the result of deliberate hard work. He was not born to it; some of his early essays are rather labored; he acquired it. He was familiar with the best Greek literature and restudied the language; he pored over Milton and Carlyle and Mill; he studied the fine old English of the Bible; he took as especial models Hume and Hobbes, until finally he wrote his mother tongue as no other Englishman wrote it. Take up any one of his essays, biological, literary, philosophical, you at once see his central idea and his main purpose, although he never uses italics or spaced letters, as many of our German masters do to relieve the obscurity of their sentences. We are carried along upon the broad current of his reasoning without being confused by

his abundant side illustrations. He gleaned
from the literature of all time until his mind
was stocked with apt similes. Who but Huxley would have selected the title "Lay Ser-
mons" for his first volume of addresses; or,
in 1880, twenty-one years after Darwin's
work appeared, would have entitled his essay
upon the influence of this work "The Coming
of Age of the Origin of Species"? Or to whom
else would it have occurred to repeat over the
grave of Balfour the exquisitely appropriate
lines: "For Lycidas is dead, dead ere his
prime"? Who else could have inveighed thus
against modern specialization:

We are in the case of Tarpeia, who opened the
gates of the Roman citadel to the Sabines and was
crushed by the weight of the reward bestowed
upon her. It has become impossible for any man
to keep pace with the progress of the whole of
any important branch of science. It looks as if
the scientific, like other revolutions, meant to
devour its own children; as if the growth of science
tended to overwhelm its votaries; as if the man
of science of the future were condemned to di-
minish into a narrow specialist as time goes on.
It appears to me that the only defense against
this tendency to the degeneration of scientific
workers lies in the organization and extension of
scientific education in such a manner as to secure

breadth of culture without superficiality; and, on the other hand, depth and precision of knowledge without narrowness.

What Haeckel did for evolution in Germany, Huxley did in England. As the earliest and most ardent supporter of Darwin and the theory of descent, it is remarkable that he never gave an unreserved support to the theory of natural selection as all-sufficient. Twenty-five years ago, with his usual penetration and prophetic insight, he showed that the problem of variation might, after all, be the greater problem; and only three years ago, in his Romanes Lecture, he disappointed many of the disciples of Darwin by declaring that natural selection failed to explain the origin of our moral and ethical nature. Whether he was right or wrong we will not stop to discuss, but consider the still more remarkable conditions of Huxley's relations to the theory of evolution. As expositor, teacher, defender, he was the high priest of evolution. From the first he saw the strong and weak points of the special Darwinian theory; he wrote upon the subject for thirty years, and yet he never contributed a single original or novel idea to it; in other words,

Huxley added vastly to the demonstration, but never added to the sum of either theory or working hypothesis, and the contemporary history of the theory proper could be written without mentioning his name. This lack of speculation upon the factors of evolution was true throughout his whole life; in the voyage of the *Rattlesnake*, he says, he did not even think of the species problem. His last utterance regarding the causes of evolution appeared in one of the reviews as a passing criticism of Weismann's finished philosophy, in which he implies that his own philosophy of the causes of evolution was as far off as ever; in other words, Huxley never fully made up his mind or committed himself to any causal theory of development.

Taking the nineteenth century at large, outside of our own circles of biology Huxley's greatest and most permanent achievement was his victory for free thought. Personally we may not be agnostic; we may disagree with much that he has said and written, but we must admire Huxley's valiant services none the less. A reformer must be an extremist, and Huxley was often extreme, but he never said what he did not believe to be true.

If it is easy for you and for me to say what we think, in print and out of print now, it is because of the battles fought by such men as Huxley and Haeckel. When Huxley began his great crusade the air was full of religious intolerance, and, what is quite as bad, scientific shams. If Huxley had entered the contest carefully and guardedly, he would have been lost in the enemies' ranks, but he struck right and left with sledge-hammer blows, whether it was a high dignitary of the church or of the state. Just before the occasion of one of his greatest contests, that with Gladstone in the pages of *The Contemporary Review*, Huxley was in Switzerland, completely broken down in health and suffering from torpidity of the liver. Gladstone had written one of his characteristically brilliant articles upon the close correspondence between the Order of Creation as revealed in the first chapter of Genesis and the Order of Evolution as shown by modern biology. "When this article reached me," Huxley told me, "I read it through and it made me so angry that I believe it must have acted upon my liver. At all events, when I finished my reply to Gladstone I felt better than I had for months past."

Huxley's last public appearance was at the meeting of the British Association at Oxford in 1894. He had been very urgently invited to attend, for, about a third of a century before, the association had met at Oxford and Huxley had had his famous encounter with Bishop Wilberforce. It was felt that the anniversary would be a historic one and incomplete without his presence, and so it proved to be. Huxley's especial duty was to second the vote of thanks for the Marquis of Salisbury's address, one of the invariable formalities of the opening meeting of the association. The meeting proved to be the greatest one in the history of the association. The Sheldonian Theatre was packed with one of the most distinguished scientific audiences ever brought together, and the address of the Marquis was worthy of the occasion. The whole tenor of it was the unknown in science. Passing from the unsolved problems of astronomy, chemistry and physics, he came to biology. With delicate irony he spoke of the "*comforting word, evolution,*" and passing to the Weismannian controversy implied that the diametrically opposed views so frequently expressed nowadays threw the whole process

of evolution into doubt. It was only too
evident that the Marquis himself found no
comfort in evolution and even entertained
a suspicion as to its probability. It was well
worth the whole journey to Oxford to watch
Huxley during this portion of the address.
In his red doctor-of-laws gown, placed upon
his shoulders by the very body of men who
had once referred to him as "a Mr. Huxley,"
he sank deeper into his chair upon the very
front of the platform and restlessly tapped his
foot. His situation was an unenviable one.
He had to thank an ex-Prime Minister of
England and present Chancellor of Oxford
University for an address the sentiments
of which were directly against those he himself had been maintaining for twenty-five
years. He said afterward that when the
proofs of the Marquis's address were put in
his hands the day before, he realized that he
had before him a most delicate and difficult
task.

Lord Kelvin (Sir William Thompson), one
of the most distinguished living physicists,
first moved the vote of thanks, but his reception was nothing to the tremendous applause
which greeted Huxley in the heart of that

might have appeared a trifle exaggerated. So you will forgive my apparent remissness in not acknowledging the receipt of it before. I do hope you will allow me to quote from your lecture, in the Life I am working upon—a long task, of which I am now somewhere about the middle.

Will you also be kind enough to tell me to what precisely you refer when you speak of my father's forming a wrong generalisation about the phylogeny of the horse? His views before or after his American visit of 1876? I do not know enough of the subject first-hand.

Once more, let me thank you for your dear & sympathetic piece of work & believe me

Sincerely yours,

(Signed)   LEONARD HUXLEY.

FRANCIS MAITLAND BALFOUR

FRANCIS MAITLAND BALFOUR

1851–1882

To Huxley and to Balfour, younger brother of Arthur Balfour, my first and most inspiring teacher in comparative embryology, I dedicated my work, "The Age of Mammals." Balfour's genius was beyond imitation, but his pupils may follow the example of his ardent enthusiasm and his genial way of living the life of science.

FRANCIS MAITLAND BALFOUR

ABOUT a year ago came the sad news of the sudden death of Professor Balfour, of Cambridge. If the loss was felt less severely in this country than in England it was only because he had fewer personal friends here, and to fully understand his worth one must have known and talked with him. It is true that it required no unusual insight to read the fine qualities of the man in his writings, but none save those who knew him could appreciate his remarkable personal attractiveness. Not the least part of the wonderful work of his short life was that which he accomplished as a teacher; here, as everywhere, his personal influence had a large share, and a sketch of Balfour's scientific work would be incomplete without a recognition of the bearing which his noble character had upon it.

The meeting of leading biologists to found the memorial studentship was remarkable in many ways; rarely have been heard such words of admiration and love for one man as

were then expressed for Balfour. Many spoke
at length of the debt Cambridge owed him.
It may be said that he divided with Foster
the honor of giving the great impetus to the
biological movement in the English universities. What Huxley had done for Foster the
latter did for Balfour, giving him the first
hearty encouragement and support; together
they raised biology from the third to the level
of the first rank of studies at Cambridge,
equalling that held by mathematics. Oxford
soon followed this important movement, trying to secure Balfour for the professorship
left vacant by the death of Rolleston. His
connection with natural science at Cambridge
was described in warm language by Foster,
his teacher, and by Sedgwick, one of his
pupils; he advanced morphology there by
his brilliant success in teaching and in research.

In teaching he combined manly force with
a delicate regard for the feelings of his pupils.
From the writer's personal impressions of
him as a lecturer, he did not aim at eloquence,
but to be understood in every step. Rarely
looking at his hearers, he spoke rapidly and
with intense earnestness, crowding a vast

deal into the hour. The main qualities of
his character shone forth in his lectures:
energy, which he infused into his hearers;
truthfulness, which soon gave implicit confidence in his statements; modesty and sympathy, which inspired effort and free exchange
of thought.

Balfour's love of truth came constantly into
play in his laboratory instruction. While
looking over a student's shoulder he would
sometimes say with a laugh: "You must interpret that specimen with the eye of faith";
but this was very far from being a serious
injunction, for he exacted of his students the
greatest caution in the progress of their micro-
scopic work. However tempting a certain
interpretation of a specimen might be, Balfour never accepted it until it rested on the
clearest evidence. An instance of this sort
is recalled which related to the much disputed
origin of a well-known embryonic structure.
A number of sections had been prepared,
seeming to confirm the view which Balfour
himself had advocated some time before; it
required considerable self-control not to at-
tach a somewhat forced meaning to them.
This was, however, forbidden, and it was not

ter contains half a dozen invitations to other investigators to prove or disprove certain provisional statements. Vast as is the information contained in his "Comparative Embryology," Balfour himself appreciated that, as far as mere facts went, the first volume would be somewhat out of date before the second was in press. Not so, however, with his masterly discussions of these facts, which are bound on every page and the value of which, to embryologists, cannot be estimated. Moreover, to his authorship is largely due the rapidly spreading interest in embryology in England and America—a branch of science, it will be remembered, which had previously been mostly in German hands.

One frequently heard from him his own very modest opinion of his work; this was not at all inconsistent with striking independence and originality of thought and adherence to his convictions. His modesty added more to the recognition of his genius than any assertions of his own could have done. Many were pressing forward to assert his claims, and honors were showered upon him in England and abroad. He was admired and beloved by all who knew him. In scientific discussion he had the rare quality, which Richard Cobden is said to have possessed, of remaining on the pleasantest personal terms with his opponents.

His energy in all matters was great and his power of writing was unusually rapid; but, advised by kind friends, he rarely overtaxed his strength, which was limited. He spent most of his evenings with his friends, throwing off from his mind the labors of the day and talking vivaciously upon the topics of the time. When the first volume of his "Comparative Embryology" was being written, he generally worked but five hours daily, giving much time to physical exercise, bicycling or tennis, into which he entered with all the enthusiasm of his nature. He was courageous but not reckless, and nothing in his previous life would lead us to suppose that the mountain climb which proved fatal was undertaken in a foolhardy spirit.

Balfour in a few years accomplished the work of a lifetime. His influence was and is twofold: first, upon those with whom he came into personal contact, especially his scientific associates and students, an influence which cannot fail to endure (well expressed by Professor Kitchen Parker: "I feel that his presence is still with me; I cannot lose the sense of his presence"); secondly, the influence of his scientific work, which for genius, breadth, and truth can never be surpassed. May the splendid memorial which has been raised for him perpetuate his noble example as a teacher and man of science.

From a photograph by Brown Brothers

JAMES BRYCE

JAMES BRYCE
1838–1922

I had the privilege of knowing James Bryce for many years and enjoyed many long and delightful conversations with him. Beyond all other great men I have known he impressed me as most eager for broad and deep knowledge both of men and of nature. He gained more by travel and direct observation than by reading the works of others.

Although an address was carefully thought out, the following was entirely extemporaneous, because I was suddenly called upon to deliver it in the pulpit of the Cathedral of St. John the Divine—quite a contrast to the customary platform of the college and university lecturer! I felt compelled by the surrounding religious atmosphere to use a text, which was happily afforded by the choir as it sang Newman's beautiful hymn as a processional.

JAMES BRYCE

I AM not permitted to have a text, because I am not a preacher. As a naturalist, I am speaking here by invitation of the Bishop and the Dean of this Cathedral on the life of James Bryce as a student of man and of nature. I find in the opening of the beautiful hymn sung by the choir on entering this Cathedral the words which I cannot resist paraphrasing as the central thought of what I am about to say: Lead, Kindly Light, amid the encircling confusion.

"Lead, Kindly Light," was the inner motive of the life of James Bryce—the kindly light of the genial nature of a man of faith and confidence, of a man of rugged resolution and constant determination, who never faltered in his efforts, whether it was a physical, or social, or intellectual, or political problem, to throw upon it the light of most careful and thorough examination.

Then another line of the same beautiful poem of John Henry Newman,

O'er moor and fen, o'er crag and torrent,

reveals the other aspect of the life of James Bryce which will impress you if you will read his four volumes as a traveler and explorer. When confused by the world and by the strife of political parties, Bryce would go off quietly on one of these great journeys of his, borne by his stout Scotch heart and by his indomitable energy as a mountain-climber. Brought up in a climate which brings out the best qualities in a man—that hardy nursery of strong Britons; born in northern Ireland, where the kindly qualities and genial nature of the Irish blend with the sturdy persistence of the Scotch, he was equipped by birth as well as by the early training of a remarkable father to enter life along many paths which opened out before him.

Follow him, no doubt somewhat confused, at the age of thirty-nine, after a period of political service in Parliament and lectureship in Oxford University, on that remarkable journey through and beyond the countries which he studied in his "Holy Roman Empire," into and through Asia Minor, into the region on the borderland of Armenia, in search of Mount Ararat, and you observe an event in his life most typical and characteristic.

Every one told him it was impossible to ascend Mount Ararat. One after another the parties that started with him fell behind, until, finally, about four or five thousand feet from the summit, he was entirely alone, and from that point he pushed on to the hollow between the twin peaks where the Bible myth tells us the Ark of Noah rested. He did not find any traces of the Ark, but he seems to have found, in that ascent and in the wonderful survey which the ascent gave him of the great tides of human history which have ebbed and flowed around the base of that mountain, a new and fresh perspective for all his future historical works. There, also, at the turning-point in life, when according to some men the critical age of forty is reached, James Bryce reversed the natural order of things, and until the age of eighty-three—during the latter part of which period I had the honor of making his acquaintance—became a younger man, a larger man, a greater man every year to all those who had the pleasure and privilege and inspiration of knowing him.

What a contrast his thoroughness with the superficiality of other men who have treated the same broad periods of human history, of human activity, and to whom many people appeal for light and guidance! Wells, writing his "Outline of History" from his armchair, guided by the work of all the authors upon whom he could lay his hand; Bryce, seeking out the fountains, the origins, the beginnings of these wonderful movements of peoples which are summed up in the words "Human History." Himself retreading the paths worn by men for centuries, observing that wonderful variety of races of men where, in entering Transcaucasia, he came on the borders between Turkey and the Russian Dominions; again, when in South Africa, he touched the life of the Kaffirs, of the Hottentots, and of that race of Bushmen which stands at the very bottom of the human scale; finally, in South America, at the age of seventy-four, he entered the intimate life of a people he had not touched before, of the Spanish, the Portuguese, the native Indians of the South American Continent—always traveling with the same genial attitude, the same kindliness, the same lack of criticism, which distinguished his life and writings throughout.

Small wonder that, having as a boy and

young man been brought up among the British people, among the Scotch, the Irish, the English, the Scotch-Irish, who are the fountains of our own American life, when he came to America he understood the Americans and was welcomed as one of us, as a man who could interpret our life, our institutions, who could tell us the truth about ourselves without our being offended, the most difficult message that any one coming from any other part of the world can give to the American!

Now we find that Bryce is not dead! James Bryce is not dead! James Bryce is living! He will live! Out of his inspiration, from those penetrating eyes, from that wonderful intellect, from those profound and unbiassed and unprejudiced studies, out of the fruits of years of personal experience, he finally surveys our American institutions in the last, and one of the greatest, of his works, "Modern Democracies." Nothing could attest the truthfulness of his nature more clearly than the fact that the note of that volume is so different from the note of his early, confident writings as a young ardent Liberal, almost Radical. He found in our midst, and in the new democracies everywhere, so many confus-

ing thoughts, so many unexpected counter-
currents, that he comes out, as does every great
and profound student of human life and human affairs who approaches the matter from
the scientific standpoint of profound knowledge, with a clear warning of the dangers
which surround us if we do not take heed and
if we lose the art of choosing our leaders, our
spiritual leaders, our intellectual leaders, our
political leaders.

Leadership! Leadership is the last note,
to my mind, of Bryce's life. He is leading.
He himself will lead because he has become
now, and I believe for all time, the Kindly
Light which will guide us through the interpretation of our American institutions.

LOUIS PASTEUR

LOUIS PASTEUR
1822–1895

To my mind Louis Pasteur is the greatest benefactor of mankind since the time of Jesus Christ, and as he was inspired by religious sentiment I claim that he should be enrolled among the saints and enshrined in our cathedrals. It is of this aspect of his life that "The New Order of Sainthood" deals. Contemplation of this aspect of his life led me to reflections upon Nature and Religion, in which I was greatly aided by my previous studies in the natural philosophy of the Greeks and of Augustine and was guided to the wonderful passages of Dante in "The Divine Comedy" by Bishop Boyd Carpenter. The sequel to this address is to be found in "Evolution and Religion," my reply to William Jennings Bryan.

THE NEW ORDER OF SAINTHOOD

AMONG all the great scientific men whom the nineteenth century produced Pasteur ranks supreme as a benefactor of mankind. He played the original and creative part in the movement for the prevention and relief of human suffering which Sir William Osler has aptly termed "Man's Redemption of Man." It is far under the truth to say that he has saved more lives than Napoleon destroyed. In nature he found the causes of a very large part of human suffering; in nature he also found the means of controlling or averting suffering. His attitude toward his fellow men was one of noble compassion. His first trial of the hydrophobia serum with a young sufferer brought to him, his agony of mind lest the remedy itself might be the means of causing death, his joy as the child was restored in perfect health to its parents, is one of the most beautiful episodes in human history. As recited by Radot, "Pasteur was going through a succession of hopes, fears, anguish, and an ardent yearning to snatch little Meister from death; he could no longer work. At night feverish visions came to him of this child, whom he had seen playing in the garden, suffocating in the mad struggles of hydrophobia, like the dying child he had seen at the Hôpital Trousseau in 1880. Vainly his experimental genius assured him that the virus of that most terrible of diseases was about to be vanquished, that humanity was about to be delivered from this dread horror—his human tenderness was stronger than all, his accustomed ready sympathy for the sufferings and anxieties of others was for the nonce centred in 'the dear lad.' . . .

"Cured from his wounds, delighted with all he saw, gayly running about as if he had been in his own Alsatian farm, little Meister, whose blue eyes now showed neither fear nor shyness, merrily received the last inoculation; in the evening, after claiming a kiss from 'Dear Monsieur Pasteur,' as he called him, he went to bed and slept peacefully."[1]

The life of Pasteur is typical of that of many students of nature, of less genius, per-

[1] Vallery-Radot, René. "The Life of Pasteur." Translation of Mrs. R. L. Devonshire. (London, Archibald Constable & Co., Ltd., 1906, pp. 416, 417.)

haps, but of equal devotion and self-sacrifice.
It is interesting to imagine what tributes
might have been rendered to Pasteur if he
had lived in the period of the early saints of
the Church and had won the love of his generation and the reverence of succeeding generations by his mighty works. It is interesting to surmise what would have been the
attitude of the early Church toward such a
benefactor of mankind. Our belief today is
that Pasteur should stand as a symbol of the
profound and intimate relation which must
develop between the study of nature and the
religious life of man, between our present and
future knowledge of nature and the development of our religious conceptions and beliefs.

In a very beautiful address[1] before the
students of the University of Edinburgh Sir
William Osler opens with the words: "To
man there has been published a triple gospel
—of his soul, of his goods, of his body."
What is and what shall be the attitude of the
Church toward the gospel of the body, toward the men who have given us this gospel?

[1] Osler, Sir Wm. "Man's Redemption of Man." 12mo. (Paul B.
Hoeber, New York.)

The question turns our thoughts at once to the leading and greatest exponent of this gospel, and backward to the early centuries of the Church before there had arisen any divorce between the study of nature and the matters of the spirit.

We are now in a process of readjustment between the issues of two lines of thought, which are almost as old as human history; between laws derived from nature which were discovered in the middle of the nineteenth century as to the origin of man, and traditional laws which when traced to their very beginnings we find to have been purely of human conception. Let us imagine our descendants three or four hundred years hence looking back on the spiritual and intellectual history of man; with larger perspective, they will separate these two grand thought-movements:

First, the Oriental movement, marked by Oriental lack of curiosity about natural law, a great moral and spiritual movement developing three thousand years before Christ along the Nile, the Tigris, and Euphrates, out of five thousand years of hard human experience, and expressed in Judea in the faith that nature is the continuous handiwork of God, in a supreme standard of righteousness, the moral duty being finally summed up in the single phrase, "Thou shalt love thy neighbor as thyself." This was the spiritual redemption of man, which left the laws of his physical welfare unknown and uncared for.

The second movement begins six centuries before Christ in the inquiring mind of the West, which is always characterized by intense curiosity about nature. This movement is the search for natural law. Its rapid progress among the Greeks terminates with the fall of Greece. It is expressed in Cato's reply to Scipio: "My wisdom consists in the fact that I follow Nature, the best of guides, as I would a God and am loyal to her commands." After nineteen centuries it revives with Copernicus and Galileo and culminates in Darwin. Man is again perceived as a part of nature; in the study of nature man finds intellectual delight; in the laws of nature man finds his physical well-being; man through nature becomes the redeemer of physical man.

The Augustinian theology was imbued with a deeply theistic view of nature, a view which the modern Church professes but does not

profoundly believe nor live by. As shown by
Aubrey Moore, Augustine was entirely sound
in counselling the entire separation of these
two great lines of thought, the natural and
the spiritual. "It very often happens," says
Augustine, "that there is some question as to
the earth or the sky, or the other elements of
this world . . . respecting which one who is
not a Christian has knowledge derived from
most certain reasoning or observation [that
is, a natural philosopher], and it is very dis-
graceful and mischievous and of all things to
be carefully avoided, that a Christian, speaking of such matters as being according to the
Christian Scriptures, should be heard by an
unbeliever talking such nonsense that the
unbeliever, perceiving him to be as wide from
the mark as east from west, can hardly restrain himself from laughing."

Augustine held what may be regarded as
a pristine faith in nature as a manifestation
of the divine. This pristine theistic view is
founded on passages in Genesis, especially
Genesis 2:15 and Genesis 3:19:

And the Lord God took the man, and put him
into the garden of Eden to dress it and to keep
it. (Genesis 2:15.)

In the sweat of thy face shalt thou eat bread, till thou return unto the ground; for out of it wast thou taken: for dust thou art, and unto dust shalt thou return. (Genesis 3:19.)

These passages show that nature, typified by the garden, gives man his sustenance, and yet, as it has to be won by the sweat of the brow, man's energy or art must work with nature. These passages, as Bishop Boyd-Carpenter observes in his inspiring studies of Dante, are also the foundation of the famous lines in the "Divine Comedy" in which the poet expresses the relation between the theistic view of nature and scientific or philosophical inquiry.

> . . . He thus made reply:
> "Philosophy, to an attentive ear,
> Clearly points out, not in one part alone,
> How imitative Nature takes her course
> From the celestial Mind, and from its art:
> And where her laws[1] the Stagirite unfolds,
> Not many leaves scann'd o'er, observing well,
> Thou shalt discover that your art on her
> Obsequious follows, as the learner treads
> In his instructor's step; so that your art
> Deserves the name of second in descent
> From God. These two, if thou recall to mind
> Creation's holy book,[2] from the beginning

[1] Aristotle ("Physics," ii, 2). "Art mimics nature."
[2] Gen. 2:15; 3:19.

Were the right source of life and excellence
To humankind. . . ."

The preceding is Cary's version.[1]   Another
version of this passage is that of Longfellow.[2]

"Philosophy," he said, "to him who heeds it,
Noteth, not only in one place alone,
After what manner Nature takes her course
From Intellect Divine and from its art;
And if thy Physics carefully thou notest,
After not many pages shalt thou find,
That this your art as far as possible
Follows, as the disciple doth the master,
So that your art is, as it were, God's grandchild.
From these two, if thou bringest to thy mind
Genesis at the beginning, it behooves
Mankind to gain their life, and to advance."

As Bishop Boyd-Carpenter remarks, Vir-
gil's answer to Dante is to this effect: We
learn from philosophy that the operations of
nature proceed directly from God, and those
of art indirectly, because art consists in the
imitation of nature.   ("Inferno," XI, pp.
97–105, Longfellow's translation.)   Again, the
Bible teaches us that it is by these two prin-

[1] "The Vision of Dante Alighieri."   Translated by the Reverend
H. F. Cary.   Canto XI, Hell, p. 47.   "Dante's Divine Comedy," with
an Introduction and Notes by Edmund G. Gardner, M.A.   (London,
J. M. Dent & Sons, Ltd.   New York, E. P. Dutton & Co.)
[2] Longfellow's Translation, Inf., Vol. XI, pp. 97–108.

ciples, nature and art, that the system of man's life should be ordered. ("Inferno," XI, pp. 106–108.)

If we are guided by the spirit of Augustine and of Dante we cannot fail to see that the Church has passed through a very critical period of scepticism as regards nature. This is perhaps an original view of scepticism, but there is no way of evading its application; if nature represents the wisdom and goodness of God, to be blind to its interpretation is a form of scepticism—devout and well-intentioned though it may be. Especially the Roman Church has been led away from its pristine faith in nature as a manifestation of the divine, while the Protestant Church, in consequence of this loss of faith during the nineteenth century, has suffered a loss of influence in the world which it will require a long period to regain. If the laws of nature are manifestations of the divine power and wisdom, as we proclaim in our services, the attitude of the Church toward these laws should not be hesitant, defensive, or apologetic, but active, receptive, and aggressive.

Considered in this way, the great scientific inquiry of the latter half of the nineteenth find one more eminent for consecration, piety, and service in life and character than this devout investigator? Entrance to this order would be granted to those who through the study of Nature have extended the bounds of human knowledge, have bestowed incomparable blessings on the human race, have relieved human suffering, have saved or prolonged human life. Would not a statue of Louis Pasteur in the Cathedral of St. John the Divine proclaim the faith of the modern Church that the two great historic movements of Love and of Knowledge, of the spiritual and intellectual and the physical well-being of man, are harmonious parts of a single and eternal truth? On the base of such a statue might be inscribed the words written by Pasteur in the most perplexing period of his life:

"GOD GRANT THAT BY MY PERSEVERING LABORS I MAY BRING A LITTLE STONE TO THE FRAIL AND ILL-ASSURED EDIFICE OF OUR KNOWLEDGE OF THOSE DEEP MYSTERIES OF LIFE AND DEATH WHERE ALL OUR INTELLECTS HAVE SO LAMENTABLY FAILED."

JOSEPH LEIDY

JOSEPH LEIDY
1823–1891

Joseph Leidy may be known as the founder of vertebrate palæontology in America, since he followed the pioneers in this branch of science, in which America has become so famous, and since he was succeeded by Edward Drinker Cope and Othniel Marsh. Leidy and Cope were the very last representatives in America of the older school of naturalists and anatomists, who covered a very broad field. They both covered this field with consummate ability. In studying Leidy's life we observe him as a master of detail, whereas Cope was a master of generalization. Their devotion to the *École des Faits* rendered most distinguished service to American science.

JOSEPH LEIDY, FOUNDER OF VERTE-BRATE PALÆONTOLOGY IN AMERICA

I ASK the indulgence of the members of this gathering in honor of Joseph Leidy and fellow workers in the fields of science if I present what I have to say in an informal manner, and I trust that you will not for a moment imagine that, because it is presented informally, I do not appreciate the honor conferred upon me in asking me to speak on this historic occasion in reference to a man for whom I have such great admiration as for Joseph Leidy. I shall not repeat except in a very general way the homage that was paid to Leidy in the series of important and penetrating addresses which we have listened to today, but I shall endeavor to present a summary, especially along the lines of palæontology and comparative anatomy, of some of the distinctive features of his work in comparison with those of the men who accompanied and immediately followed him, and to show what great results have come from his efforts as a pioneer and as a founder of this most interesting and fascinating branch of science in America.

Leidy started with an entirely new world of life; he soon learned that he could not base his study of American fossils on the work of French palæontologists, for the life of our western regions was not known in the Old World. Every specimen represented a new species or a new genus or a new family, and in some cases a new order. Never was there a greater opportunity than was offered to Leidy in this virgin field of our then virgin West. Never was a man more ready to grasp it than that quiet, unpretentious, unassuming, wonderfully gifted observer of nature. It is particularly interesting to review his work, which was written in the exact spirit of Cuvier, and to see his long record of direct observation of the entire extinct fauna not only of the eastern but, especially, of the great western territories. We find today how permanent that work was, how little we have to modify it, how well it stands the test of time, how accurate are his descriptions, how perfect his figures and illustrations, and how even today they form admirable standards for all the work that has been done since. After a continuous series of epoch-making papers and contributions which he was in the habit of contributing year after year, in meeting after meeting of the academy, he brought his initial work to a climax in 1869 when he published his great monograph, "Extinct Mammalian Fauna of Nebraska and Dakota." That work still ranks in breadth and accuracy as the finest single contribution that has been made to vertebrate palæontology in this country, if not in the world.

Whereas in Leidy we had a man of the exact observer type, Cope was a man who loved speculation. If Leidy was the natural successor of Cuvier, Cope was the natural successor of Lamarck. Leidy, in his contributions to the academy, covered the whole world of nature, from the Protozoa and Infusoria up to man, and he lived as the last great naturalist in the world of the old type who was able by both capacity and training to cover the whole field of nature. Cope, in contrast, mastered—and this mastery in itself was a wonderful achievement—the entire domain of vertebrates from the fishes up.

Marsh, with less breadth and less ability, nevertheless was a palæontologist of a very high order and had a genius for appreciating what might be called the most important thing in science. He always knew where to explore, where to seek the transition stages, and he never lost the opportunity to point out at the earliest possible moment the most significant fact to be discovered and disseminated.

It is most interesting to contrast the temperament of these three men, Joseph Leidy, Edward Drinker Cope, and Othniel Charles Marsh. They were as different as any three men could possibly be made, both by nature and nurture. As Professor Edward Smith said, in one of his addresses on Leidy, "scientists are only mortals after all." Your scientific genius may hitch up with a star on the one hand and with an anchor on the other. Whereas Leidy was essentially a man of peace, Cope was what might be called a militant palæontologist. Whereas Leidy's motto was peace at any price, Cope's was war whatever it cost. I do not know that I can find from Shakespeare any characterization of Joseph Leidy, but I think in "Henry IV" there is a

pretty good characterization of my friend
Edward D. Cope:

I am not yet of Percy's mind, the Hotspur of the
north; he that kills me some six or seven dozen of
Scots at a breakfast, washes his hands, and
says to his wife, "Fie upon this quiet life! I
want work."

Perhaps there was a scientific providence
in all this; perhaps such antagonistic spirits
were necessary to enliven and disseminate
interest in this branch of science throughout
the country. This subtle combative quality
in a palæontologist is a strange quality; it is
a strange inversion, because the more ancient
and difficult the study, the more refractory
the fossil, the greater the animation of discussion regarding its relationships. From this
subtle ferment there arose the famous rivalry
which existed not between Leidy and either
of the others, because it was impossible to
quarrel with Leidy, but between Cope, the
descendant of a Quaker family, and Marsh,
the nephew of a great philanthropist. When
I took up the subject as a young man and
first came to the City of Brotherly Love I
always expected to learn of some fresh discussion, some recent combat; it was even in

the shade of the Academy of Natural Sciences
that one found echoes of these convulsive
movements. I remember one day coming
into the dignified halls of the academy and
finding two of the youthful attendants engaged in hot discussion over a dispute they
had overheard at a meeting of the academy
the night before.

Leidy, after the characterizations that we
have heard of his life from Conklin, Jennings,
Scott and others, occupied a pivotal position,
a very interesting pivotal position. He was
in an intellectual environment and more or
less in a social environment entirely different
from our own. This is very important to
keep in mind in estimating his work. In
spirit he was, I think, a true pre-Darwinian
in the sense of seeking what may be called
facts for Darwin and in the breadth and scope
of his researches. But he lived in an entirely
different intellectual atmosphere from that
which surrounds our scientific world of today; he was a John the Baptist for Charles
Darwin. We must remember that twelve
years before Darwin brought forth the "Origin of Species" this young man was beginning
to assemble a mass of data which would have

been of great value to the great British naturalist. As shown by Professor Scott, he was
tracing the ancestral lineage of the horse, the
camel, the rhinoceros, the tapir family, the
titanotheres, and last, but not least, the anatomical forebears of man.

Nevertheless, Leidy was an evolutionist
sub rosa; he was an evolutionist without ever
using the word evolution. There is no doubt
about that when you read a citation from his
writings such as was selected by Professor
Jennings:

The study of the earth's crust teaches us that
very many species of plants and animals became
extinct at successive periods, while other races
originated to occupy their places. This probably
was the result, in many cases, of a change in exte-
rior conditions incompatible with the life of certain species and favorable to the primitive production of others. . . . Living beings did not
exist upon the earth prior to their indispensable
conditions of action, but wherever these have been
brought into operation concomitantly, the former
originated. . . . Of the life, present everywhere
with its indispensable conditions, and coeval in
its origin with them, what was the immediate
cause? It could not have existed upon earth
prior to its essential conditions; and is it, therefore, the result of these? There appear to be
but trifling steps from the oscillating particles of

inorganic matter to a bacterium; from this to a
vibrio, thence to a monas, and so gradually up
to the highest orders of life! The most ancient
rocks containing remains of living beings indicate
the contemporaneous existence of the more complex as well as the simplest of organic forms; but,
nevertheless, life may have been ushered upon
earth, through oceans of the lowest types, long
previously to the deposit of the oldest palæozoic
rocks as known to us.

This really is a sketch in 1847 of environment and survival such as we now know to
be the actual course of evolution and was
truly anticipatory of modern results, substi-
tuting modern language as we may do for the
quaint phraseology of the period.

On the subject of the evolution of man
especially Leidy certainly had very clear and
positive ideas. He caught from Goethe the
significance of the occasional reversion and
the embryonic suture between the premaxil-
lary and maxillary bones—constituting a single bone in the human subject, two bones in
the lower order of mammals. He pointed out
this suture in 1847 in the skull of a native
from one of the Hollander Islands. In 1849
he pointed out the separate embryonic condition of the intermaxillary bones. In both

cases, as was his habit, Leidy obviously saw the significance but, always sticking to facts and a presentation of facts, he let the matter rest there. The most pronounced adumbration, however, of the evolution of man from the primates is to be found in a citation of his volume of 1873, a period when the descent of man was still not recognized:

But little change would be necessary to evolve from the jawbone and teeth of *Notharctus* that of the modern monkey. The same condition that would lead to the suppression of a first premolar tooth in continuance would reduce the fangs of the other premolars to a single one. This change with the common teeth shortening and the increase of the depth of the jaw would give the character of the living South American monkey. A further reduction would give rise to the condition of the jaw in the Old World apes and in man.

I do not need to point out that the human jaw, next to the human forehead, is the most significant feature in the transformation from the lower to the higher primates. But some of those here present may not know that a monograph has been written by my successor and colleague, Professor William K. Gregory, upon the genus *Notharctus* Leidy. Gregory, fifty years after this significant passage was written by Leidy, chose *Notharctus* as an ideal intermediate type to place in a theoretic ancestral series leading up to man, and in the beautiful series of preparations which he has recently completed showing the development of the human face in all stages from the most remote ancestral facial type to the modern human face, Gregory uses *Notharctus* as the pivotal point, just as did Leidy fifty years ago.

To return to the matter of Leidy's intellectual environment: how much we owe to-day to our intellectual environment, how much we owe to battles which have been fought and won over insufficient evidence! Not battles of words, but battles of facts. Such evidence as that of *Notharctus* the alert vision of Leidy detected and put in its proper place. In those days "mum" was the word as regards evolution. Neither Cuvier nor Owen, the British successor of Cuvier, nor Louis Agassiz, great naturalists all, had accepted the theory; theologic influence was still all-powerful. Fortunately for Leidy, William Jennings Bryan was still in embryo. Trying to form an historic parallel of William Jennings Bryan, I think it may be found in the figure of King Canute sitting with his court on the shores of Nature, trying to beat back the waves of Truth. If Leidy had lived in the era of Bryan, he undoubtedly would have been classified with Professor Conklin and myself—he would have been made with us a type of a new genus, *Anathema maranatha*, in which, according to the zoology of Bryan, are embraced "tall professors coming down out of trees who would push good people not believing in evolution off the sidewalk." Leidy would not have been burned at the stake, only because of legal obstacles. Similarly, I think that Professor Conklin and myself owe our lives to the fact that *autos da fé* in matters of belief are no longer matters of common practice in our civilization!

It is perhaps particularly fitting that Professor Scott and myself were asked to speak at this centenary, for one reason above others. We have been the defendants and supporters of the Leidy tradition. I am not quite sure, but I doubt if you will find in the writings of Professor Cope or Professor Marsh a single allusion to the work of Leidy. I make this statement subject to verification, but I do not recall in their writings a single allusion to the work of Leidy, except a brief tribute by Marsh in an early address; the rivalry between the two men went to such lengths that in their race with each other Leidy was totally forgotten. Every new animal that was discovered was given a new scientific name by each of them. *Notharctus* Leidy, for example, is exactly the same animal as *Tomitherium* Cope and *Limnotherium* Marsh. Thus arose a trinominal system—three names each for the Eocene and Oligocene animals—the original Leidy name and the Cope and Marsh names. It has been the painful duty of Professor Scott and myself to devote thirty of the best years of our lives trying to straighten out this nomenclatural chaos. Even to this day we are verifying the observations of Leidy; we find that he never made an incorrect observation or published an incorrect figure; his accuracy in these regards is one of his greatest and most permanent claims to immortality as a palæontologist.

I do not know that I altogether agree with my friend Conklin in his address as to the relation of extensive and intensive work. If I understand him aright, he rather implies that intensive work is an inevitable feature of modern scientific progress. I would rather cite Leidy as an example of a man who pursued intensive work and extensive work simultaneously and who had the capacity to pursue intensive work in several branches of science, biological and geological, and I would regard the permanence of Leidy's work as largely the result of the state of mind produced by the breadth of his intensive as well as of his extensive work. I would like to leave on your minds my conviction, buttressed by Leidy's life, that it will be necessary even for those of our day to maintain the Leidy attitude, because, after all, it is in *the single mind that great hypotheses and theories are generated*. The comparative anatomist, if he dies out, will leave human anatomy impoverished. Today our students should return to the Leidy attitude, as Professor Scott said, of entering palæontology by way of medicine and base our education in human anatomy, as Leidy did, on a broad knowledge of comparative anatomy. This is only one instance out of very many that might be given of the legacies of Leidy to us: namely, that throughout his life his mind had continuously the intensive as well as the extensive attitude. He was able to be on the moun-

tain-top and then descend into the valley, and
I believe that while some men who pursue
one subject intensively all their lives are
making great discoveries, for example, such
workers as Professor Michelson, whom we
all honor, the chances are that few men can
make great discoveries unless they approach
the subject broadly and work from more than
one angle of thought.

Speaking of immortality, I share rather the
Leidy view than the view of Cope. I wish
it were possible to resurrect Joseph Leidy
and to bring him back into the field of modern American palæontology. I wish it were
possible to bring him back to life and to have
taken him with me, for example, in a motor-
car across the wastes of Mongolia. I can
imagine the joy with which he would have
welcomed coming upon the remains of the
land dinosaurs, recalling his first description
of a dinosaur in America, in the very heart
of the great Desert of Gobi; and perhaps the
still greater joy with which he would have
greeted one of his titanotheres, one of the
first mammals which he described from Wyoming, out on a great plain on the border of
the Desert of Gobi.

The desire for this kind of immortality reminds me often of the Greek poet:

To live like man and yet like nature to endure,
That double gift, to man and nature both denied,
The Gods alone enjoy.

We are rewriting this beautiful Greek verse in the immortality of Leidy's work, and we are holding up his example for the prevailing spirit of truthfulness, which is, after all, its most characteristic single feature. Would that Leidy and Huxley and Richard Owen and Cuvier and Marsh and Cope could see the heights which have been reached in the branch of science to which they devoted their lives and fortunes. Leidy's infant science, in which it was most hazardous to make predictions, has now reached the stage which I believe is the finest in the history of any science—the stage of prediction—that, as astronomers have predicted the existence of unknown and unseen planets, palæontologists can also predict unknown and unseen forms of life and, moreover, can point out where they may be found.

Is our palæontological path reaching its goal? I think not. Its final goal will be reached when palæontologists are able through

extensive and intensive methods to join hands
with workers in other biological fields and
when we are able, pursuing our branch in the
Leidy spirit, to bring together into one harmony—the harmony which certainly exists,
although at present we do not see it—by
bringing together into one harmony the great
underlying principle, the multiple aspects of
which we can sum up in the word "evolution."

From a photograph by Gutekunst

EDWARD DRINKER COPE

EDWARD DRINKER COPE
1840–1897

Undoubtedly the most brilliant palæontologist of America and one of the most brilliant scientists America has produced. This biography fittingly follows that of Joseph Leidy, although there is the greatest possible contrast between the life and works of the two men: Cope, brilliant, daring, combative; Leidy, patient, persistent, cautious, conservative. It was a contrast between the temperamental Gaelic and the stable Teutonic type. The work of both men will endure for all time. That of Cope requires constant emendation and revision, but it leaves a firm and broad foundation for our knowledge of the evolution of the vertebrata. Leidy was a master of detail, of accurate description, of finished workmanship, rarely venturing generalization, but he left a treasure-house of splendidly collected facts.

The work of Professor Cope began in 1859, a most favorable year, when comparative anatomy first felt the impetus of Darwin's "Origin of Species." He was then only nineteen, and for thirty-eight years thereafter his active genius hastened our progress in the knowledge and classification of all the great divisions of the vertebrata. He passed away on April 12, 1897, at the age of fifty-seven, in the full vigor of his intellectual powers, leaving a large part of his work incomplete. Almost at the last he contributed several reviews to *The American Naturalist*, and on the Tuesday preceding his death he sent to the press the Syllabus of his lectures before the University of Pennsylvania, containing his latest opinions regarding the arrangement and evolution of the vertebrata.

A GREAT NATURALIST

EDWARD DRINKER COPE was born in Philadelphia July 28, 1840, of distinguished American ancestry. His grandfather, Caleb Cope, was the staunch Quaker of Lancaster, Pennsylvania, who protected Major André from mob violence. Thomas Pim Cope, his grandfather, founded the house of Cope Brothers, famous in the early mercantile annals of Philadelphia. His father, Alfred, the junior member of the firm, was a man of very active intellect and showed rare judgment in Edward's education.

Together the father and son became brisk investigators, the father stimulating by questions and by travel the strong love of nature and of natural objects which the son showed at an unusually early age. In August, 1857, they took a sea voyage to Boston, and the son's journal is full of drawings of jellyfish, grampuses, and other natural objects seen by the way. When eight and a half years old he made his first visit to the Museum of the Academy of Natural Sciences, "on the 21st day of the 10th Mo., 1848," as entered in his journal. He brought away careful drawings, measurements, and descriptions of several larger birds, but especially the figure of the entire skeleton of an ichthyosaur, with this quaint memorandum: "Two of the sclerotic plates look at the eye—thee will see these in it." At the age of ten he was taken upon a longer voyage to the West Indies. It is not improbable that these voyages exerted a lasting influence upon him.

The principal impression he gave in boy-hood was of incessant activity in mind and body, of quick and ingenious thought, reaching in every direction for knowledge, and of great independence in character and action. It is evident that he owed far more to the direct study of nature and to his own impulses as a young investigator than to the five or six years of formal education which he received at school. He was especially fond of map drawing and of geographical studies. His natural talent for languages may have been cultivated in some degree by his tutor, Dr. Joseph Thomas, an excellent linguist, editor of a biographical dictionary. Many of his spare winter hours were passed at the

Academy of Natural Sciences. After the age
of thirteen the summer intervals of boarding-
school life and later of tutoring were filled
among the woods, fields, and streams of Chester County, Pennsylvania, where an intimate
knowledge of birds was added to that of ba-
trachians, reptiles, and insects. He showed
a particular fondness for snakes. One of
these excursions, taken at the age of nineteen, is described in a letter to his cousin
(dated June 24, 1859), in which, at the close
of a charming description of the botany of
the region, appears his discovery of a new
type:

I traced the stream for a very considerable
distance upon the rocky hillside, my admiration
never ceasing, but I finally turned off into the
woods towards some towering rocks. Here I
actually got to searching for salamanders and was
rewarded by capturing two specimens of species
which I never saw before alive. The first (*Spelerpes longicauda*) is a great rarity here. I am
doubtful of its having been previously noted in
Chester County. Its length is 6 inches, of which
its tail forms nearly four. The color is deep
brownish yellow thickly spotted with black, which
becomes confluent on the tail, thus forming bands.
To me a very interesting animal—the type of the
genus *Spelerpes*, and consequently of the subfamily

Spelerpinæ, which I attempted to characterize in a paper published in the *Proceedings of the Academy of Natural Sciences*. I send thee a copy, with the request that thee will neither mention nor show it,[1] for—however trifling—I would doubtless be miserably annoyed by some if thee should. Nobody in this country (or in Europe, of *ours*) knows anything about salamanders, but Professor Baird and thy humble coz., that is, in some respects. Rusconi, the only man who has observed their method of reproduction, has written enough to excite greatly one's curiosity and not fully satisfy it. With suitable appliances of aquariums, etc., I should like to make some observations. The other salamander I caught was *Plethodon glutinosum*—the young—remarkable for the great number of teeth that lie together in two patches on the "basisphenoid" bone; about 300 or more.

Another passage gives an insight into his strong opinion, so often expressed afterward, as to what constitutes the real pleasures of life:

Pleasant it is, too, to find one whose admiration of nature and detail is heightened, not chilled, by the necessary "investigation"—which, in my humble opinion, is one of the most useful as well as pleasing exercises of the intellect, in the circle of human study. How many are there who are de-

---

[1] This passage probably indicates that he was sensitive to being laughed at for his interest in these animals.

lighted with a "fine view," but who seldom care to
think of the mighty and mysterious agency that
reared the hills, of the wonderful structure and
growth of the forests that crown them, or of the
complicated mechanism of the myriads of higher
organisms that abound everywhere; who would
see but little interesting in a fungus, and who
would shrink with affected horror from a defenseless toad.

Having passed six summers among the
woods and streams of Chester County, Pennsylvania, it is not surprising to find him, at
the time this letter was written, perfectly
familiar with the plants, birds, snakes, and
salamanders of eastern Pennsylvania, and
perfectly aware of the rarity of such knowledge. His range extended with astonishing
rapidity; first among the living reptiles and
amphibians; then among living and palæozoic fishes; then among the great extinct
reptiles of New Jersey and the Rocky Mountains; finally among the ancient American
quadrupeds. He acquired in turn a masterly
knowledge of each type. Irreverent toward
old systems, eager and ambitious to replace
them by new ones of his own, with unbounded
powers of hard work, whether in the field or
at his desk, he rapidly became a leading

spirit among the workers in the great realm of
the backboned creation, both in America
and Europe. While inferior in logic, he
showed Huxley's unerring vision of the most
distinctive feature in a group of animals, as
well as the broad grasp of Cuvier and of Cuvier's famous English disciple, Owen. While
most men of our day are able to specialize
among the details of an order, or at most of
a class, Cope, at the age of thirty-four, had
in his mental horizon at once the five great
classes, although since Owen's time they had
been greatly expanded by palæontological
discovery. He was thus the last and most
distinguished representative of the old school
of comparative anatomists. His high pressure of thirty-eight years' work was not
consistent with excelling accuracy. We have
often to look behind the returns in using
Cope's work. Yet if it lacks German exact-
ness, French beauty of presentation, and the
solidity which marks the best English scientific workmanship, its dominant principles
are sound and its chief anatomical generalizations will endure longer than those of either
Owen or Cuvier.

With this peculiar fitness for great studies

came first the glorious opportunity of entering the unknown western field as a pioneer with Marsh and Leidy. In 1866 he was the first to find along the New Jersey coast remains of the leaping dinosaur, *Lælaps aquilunguis*, and he anticipated Huxley in comparing these reptiles with the birds. In 1871 he extended his explorations westward into what is now the most arid portion of Kansas, among the remains of the ancient marine monsters, the ram-nosed mosasaur and the sea-serpent, or elasmosaur. Following up the rapid advance of government exploration in the Rocky Mountains between 1872 and 1878, he discovered in New Mexico, Colorado, and Wyoming the great amphicœlias, the gigantic camarasaurus, and the frill-necked dinosaur agathaumas. As a pioneer in exploration among these giant animals he was obliged to draw his conclusions largely from fragmentary and imperfect materials, leaving the field open to Professor Marsh's more exhaustive explorations, which were supported by the government. Yet Professor Cope illuminated the incomplete fragments with his reasoning and his fertile imagination. When a bone came into his hands, his first step was to turn it over and over, to comprehend its form thoroughly, and to compare it with its nearest ally, then to throw out a conjecture as to its uses and its relation to the life economy of the animal as a whole. One often found him virtually living in the past, vividly picturing to himself the muddy shores of the Permian seas of Texas, where the fin-back lizards basked, or the great fresh-water expanses of Wyoming and Montana, where the dinosaurs wandered. His conclusions as to the habits and modes of locomotion of these animals, often so grotesque as to excite laughter, were suggestive revivals from the vast deeps of time of the muscular and nervous life which once impelled the mighty bones. It is fortunate that some of this imaginative history has been written down by Mr. Ballou and that, although physically enfeebled by a mortal illness, Professor Cope in his last days was able to convey to Mr. Knight, the artist, his impressions of how these ancient saurians lived and moved.

The second feature of his opportunity was, of course, that this pioneer exploration came early in the age of Darwinism, when missing links, not only in human ancestry, but in the

greater chain of backboned animals, were at
the highest premium. Thus he was fortunate
in recording the discovery in northwestern
New Mexico of by far the oldest quadrupeds
known, in finding among these the most
venerable monkey, in describing to the world
hundreds of links—in fact, whole chains—of
descent between the most ancient quadrupeds
and what we please to call the higher types,
especially the horses, camels, tapirs, dogs, and
cats. He labored successfully to connect the
reptiles with the amphibians and the latter
with the fishes, and was as quick as a flash
to detect in the paper of another author the
oversight of some long-sought link which he
had been awaiting. Thus in losing him we
have lost our ablest and most discerning
critic. No one has made such profuse and
overwhelming demonstration of the actual
historical working of the laws of evolution,
his popular reputation perhaps resting most
widely upon his practical and speculative
studies in evolution.

Many friends in this country and abroad
have spoken of the invigorating nature of
his companionship. A life of intense activity,
harassed for long periods by many difficulties

and obstacles, many of them of his own making, was nevertheless wholly without worry,
that destroyer of the mind so common in our
country. His half-century's enjoyment of
research, extending from his seventh to his
fifty-seventh year, can only be described in
its effects upon him as buoyant; it lifted him
far above disturbance by the ordinary matters of life, above considerations of physical
comfort and material welfare, and animated
him with a serene confidence in the rewards
which Science extends to her votaries. He
exemplified the truth of the words which
Peacock puts into the meditation of Asterius:

. . . while science moves on in the calm dignity
of its course, affording to youth delights equally
pure and vivid—to maturity, calm and grateful
occupation—to old age, the most pleasing recollections and inexhaustible materials of agreeable
and salutary reflection; and while its votary en-
joys the disinterested pleasure of enlarging the
intellect and increasing the comforts of society,
he is himself independent of the caprices of human
intercourse and the accidents of human fortune.
Nature is his great and inexhaustible treasure.
His days are always too short for his enjoyment;
ennui is a stranger to his door. At peace with the
world and with his own mind, he suffices to himself, makes all around him happy, and the close of

his pleasing and beneficial existence is the evening
of a beautiful day.

While working at Cope's museum-residence
at Philadelphia, I have had many queer experiences in the odd, half-Bohemian restaurants
which the naturalist frequented. The quality
of the meal was a secondary consideration
to him, provided it afforded sufficient brain
fuel. While eating he always relaxed into
pure fun and displayed a large fund of amusing anecdotes of the experiences, mishaps, and
frailties of scientists, his own as often as those
of others. He worked deliberately and gave
his whole mind to one subject at a time, if
he considered it of special importance, this
power being aided by his remarkable memory
of species and of objects long laid aside for
future reference. In his field exploration his
scientific enthusiasm burned still higher in
pursuit of an unknown type or a missing
link. Neither horses nor men could keep pace
with his indefatigable energy. Heat and al-
kali-water were totally disregarded. From
one of his Bitter Creek Desert trips he returned to Fort Bridger completely exhausted
and for weeks was prostrated with fever.

Only a short time before his death he laughingly related that after a solemn warning by a physician to avoid horse-back riding and exposure to water, his health had been greatly improved in the course of a summer by three hundred miles' exercise in the saddle in North Dakota and several weeks' wading in New Jersey swamps. His house in Pine Street became every year a greater curiosity as the accumulating fossils, books, and pamphlets outtaxed the shelves and began to thicken like stratified deposits upon the floor in dust-laden walls and lanes. Even his sleeping-room was piled to the ceiling, and he closed his eyes for the last time while lying upon a bed surrounded on three sides by the loved objects of his life-work.

The most conspicuous feature of Cope's character from boyhood upward was independence; this was partly the secret of his venturesome and successful assaults upon all traditional but defective systems of classification. Seldom has a face reflected a character more fully than that of Professor Cope. His square and prominent forehead suggested his vigorous intellect and marvelous memory; his brilliant eyes were the media of exceptional keenness of observation; his prominent chin was in traditional harmony with his aggressive spirit. From this rare combination of qualities so essential to free investigation sprang his scientific genius, and, with exceptional facilities of wealth and culture in his early education, he became a great naturalist—certainly the greatest America has produced.

As a comparative anatomist he ranks both in the range and effectiveness of knowledge and ideas with Cuvier and Owen. When we consider the short life of some of the favorite generalizations of these great men he may well prove to be their superior as a philosophical anatomist. His work, while inferior in style of presentation, has another quality, which distinguishes that of Huxley, namely, its clear and immediate perception of the most essential or distinctive features in a group of animals. As a natural philosopher, while far less logical than Huxley, he was more creative and constructive, his metaphysics ending in theism rather than in agnosticism.

Cope is not to be thought of merely as a specialist. After Huxley he was the last representative of the old broad-gauge school of anatomists, and he is only to be compared with members of that school. His life-work

bears the marks of great genius, of solid and
accurate observation as well as of inaccuracy
due to bad logic or haste and overpressure of
work. Although the greater number of his
Natural Orders and Natural Laws will remain as permanent landmarks in our science,
a large part of his systematic work will require laborious revision and thus is far from
standing as a model to the young zoologist.

Appreciation of greatness is a mark of the
civilization and culture of a people. Cope's
monumental work, preserved in thousands of
notes, short papers, and memoirs, and in three
bulky government quartos, constitutes his
assurance of enduring fame. Some of his
countrymen, and even of his fellow-workers,
allowed certain of his characteristics to obscure his stronger side in their estimate of
him and his work, and during his life he received few of the honors such as foreigners
are wont to bestow upon their countrymen
of note. When we think more deeply of what
really underlies human progress, we realize
that only to a few men with the light of genius
is it given to push the world's human thought
along, and that Edward Drinker Cope was
one of these men.

From a photograph copyright by Underwood and Underwood

THEODORE ROOSEVELT

THEODORE ROOSEVELT
1858–1919

In his early life Roosevelt was a warm friend and companion of my naturalist brother, Frederick. During the last ten years of his life I became very intimate with him, especially after the writing of my "Age of Mammals" in 1910, which he read with ardor. Recalling his experiences as Police Commissioner of the City of New York, in writing to me of this book he said he enjoyed comparing certain politicians with whom he was thrown with the hyænodons and certain less desirable animal citizens of the Tertiary age! It was perhaps this running parallel between human nature and animal nature which grew on his mind and caused him to seek my advice when invited to prepare and deliver the Romanes Lecture at Oxford, which he entitled "Biological Analogies in History." He was more kinds of a man than any one I have ever known—that is, able in more lines.

In this "Impression" I endeavor to show that the scientific side of Roosevelt's life is to be taken seriously; that he had unusual ability as a naturalist and observer, which would have led to a distinguished career in science had he not been turned to government. Above all things he desired to be truthful and strictly accurate, and he took infinite pains not to exaggerate but to present the real facts.

THEODORE ROOSEVELT
NATURALIST

"Do what you can, where you are, with what you have."
—ROOSEVELT.

THEODORE ROOSEVELT doubtless inherited his natural history bent from his father, who was a founder of the American Museum of Natural History in the year 1869. I had the good fortune to recall young Theodore in his boyhood, because of no life may it more truly be said that "the child is father of the man." He was one of a youthful band of bird-lovers, observers and collectors, among whom was my brother Frederick, who came together in the seventies. While Frederick confined himself to birds, Theodore was interested also in mammals and small amphibians, and he came back from their collecting trips with all kinds of specimens. Frederick invited Theodore to collect birds with him in the forests of the Hudson River highlands, and on one occasion, when every pocket was full of specimens, Theodore suddenly discovered what he be-

ing experience he was constantly observing
the western game mammals and he made extensive contributions to our knowledge of
their habits and distribution. Birds were his
first love, and by far the most thorough
knowledge which he displayed was in the field
of ornithology; he knew not only the birds
and their songs but also all their scientific
names. Lord Grey, in an address to the Harvard students, verified this statement of
Roosevelt's unusual knowledge of birds, British as well as American. Walking through the
New Forest together they observed upward
of thirty species of birds, each of which Theodore Roosevelt knew by familiar and scientific name, recognizing many of them by what
he had read of their songs.

Among extinct animals, in which I am especially interested, Roosevelt was not an original observer, but he was a voracious reader
of everything worth while written about them
and soon became extremely well informed.
In this connection I recall an amusing and
characteristic incident. Receiving an invitation to deliver one of the Romanes Lectures
at Oxford—perhaps the greatest lectureship
of the kind in the world—Roosevelt wrote

to me, as follows, for advice as to whether he
could do it and should do it:

I have just received from Lord Curzon, the
Chancellor of Oxford, a request to deliver the
Romanes Lecture at any time I see fit. I shall
probably accept for the spring that I get out of
Africa on my way back to the United States. It
seems to me worth while for me to do so. Doesn't
it seem so to you? It is a lecture which has been
delivered by Gladstone, Huxley, John Morley,
Bryce, and other men of that stamp.

I replied in the affirmative on both questions
and he immediately wrote back that he would
prepare the lecture on condition that I would
read it over and make corrections, since it
was my peculiar field of work. At that time
he was President of the United States, nearing
the end of his term and engaged in a tremendous struggle with both the Senate and the
House, on which for the time he had apparently lost his hold. This political preoccupation, however, did not prevent his preparing
three very important addresses which he had
been asked to deliver, in Berlin, in Paris, and
that above mentioned in Oxford.

In a relatively short time I received the
manuscript of his Romanes Lecture. It was

heard Roosevelt, and in the way of grading which we have at Oxford we agreed to mark the lecture 'beta minus' but the lecturer 'alpha plus.' While we felt that the lecture was not a very great contribution to science we were sure that the lecturer was a very great man, to be ranked in the plus A class. After the lecture Colonel Roosevelt asked me how I liked it. I may have expressed rather qualified admiration and seeing my hesitation he said: 'Well, that lecture would have been a great deal stronger had not one of my scientific friends in America *blue-penciled the best part of it.*' "

While perhaps strongest in his knowledge of birds, Theodore Roosevelt also gained an extraordinary knowledge of mammals, especially of North America and of Africa. In preparing for his African trip he called upon me for all the books I could supply from the Osborn Library in the American Museum, which in many respects is one of the most complete in the country, if not in the world. For several weeks he consumed five books a week, sitting up to the small hours of the morning to complete his reading or until Mrs. Roosevelt insisted upon his retiring.

Thus in the course of a few weeks he had read all that had been written about the great mammals of Africa from Sclater to Selous. He read so rapidly that it did not seem possible that he could absorb it all, yet when we gathered at Sagamore Hill to talk over his expedition—a group of the very best naturalists familiar with African life whom he could get together for luncheon—he displayed a knowledge of the genera and species and of the precise localities where each might be found which was equal or superior to that of any man in the room. To cite only one instance of his marvelous memory and of his thoroughness of preparation: a question arose as to the locality of a particular subspecies, Grevy's zebra (*Equus grevyi foai*). Roosevelt went to the map, pointed out directly the particular and only spot where it could be found and said that he thought the expedition could not possibly get down in that direction.

Equipped with this knowledge and aided by three or four exceptional men like Heller and Akeley, he conducted, under the auspices of the Smithsonian Institution, by far the most successful expedition that has ever penetrated Africa, the chief collections from at home. Briefly rehearsing his experiences abroad, he said that he was far more gratified by his reception at home and welcome to America than by any of the acclamation he had received abroad. Then, lowering his voice and his head, he continued:

But, my friends—you all are my friends—I am not deceived for one moment. I know the American people; they have a way of erecting a triumphal arch, and after the Conquering Hero has passed beneath it he may expect to receive a shower of bricks on his back at any moment! Yes, my friends, I am having a bully time. I am swimming on the very crest of the wave and enjoying it immensely, but I am not for a moment deceived; next week or next month I may be again in the trough of the wave, but I assure you I shall be swimming just as hard and enjoying life just as much as I now am.

None of his friends at that time believed that such a prophecy could possibly be realized, yet it came true with amazing suddenness. Within a few weeks his name had apparently left the headlines for good; it appeared only in small type in brief paragraphs on inside pages. To the superficial observer, to those who did not know the real Roosevelt and his powers of resilience his career was ended.

The lull in publicity gave him the quiet he needed to devote to three volumes of natural history and to prepare for his last and altogether greatest period of exploration. His manifold ability and the marked characteristics of his multiple personality came out in the course of his plans for the great expedition to South America projected in the spring of 1913 and executed between October, 1913, and June, 1914. He had selected an unknown and particularly dangerous region, where the native tribes had never been thoroughly subdued by the Brazilian government. He marked out this region as his first choice for a South American expedition. I sent word to him through our mutual friend, Frank M. Chapman, that I would never consent to his going to this particular region under the American Museum flag, that I would not assume even part of the responsibility for his entering such a dangerous country and not returning alive. With a smile he sent back to me through Chapman a characteristic reply:

Tell Osborn I have already lived and enjoyed as much of life as any nine other men I know; I have had my full share, and if it is necessary

for me to leave my bones in South America, I am
quite ready to do so.

Although more prudent plans prevailed
and we finally determined upon a route which
resulted in the discovery of the Rio Roosevelt, yet the exposure, the excessively moist
climate, the dearth of food, clothing and sup-
plies, and the malarial infection very nearly
cost Roosevelt his life. There is no doubt
that the hazard of the trip meant nothing
to him. While never reckless, he was absolutely fearless. His plans were made with
the utmost intelligence and thoroughness, and
with the trained assistance of his son Kermit,
the South American experience and stal-
wart courage of George K. Cherrie, and the
devoted companionship of Colonel Candido
Mariano da Silva Rondon and Leo E. Miller,
he led the most important expedition that
has ever gone from North into South America.
As a result of this expedition through Para-
guay and the wilderness of Brazil more than
450 mammal and 1375 bird specimens were
added to the American Museum collections,
in addition to the geographic results, which
aroused such a chorus of discussion and diver-

sity of opinion. Roosevelt was so impressed
with the importance of continuing the exploration that on his return he personally
contributed two thousand dollars from his
literary earnings to send his companion
naturalists back to the field.

An American statesman, who should have
known better, once characterized Roosevelt
as "one who knew a little about more things
than any one else in this country." This
gives an entirely false impression of Roosevelt's mind, which was of quite the contrary
order. What Roosevelt did know in history
and in natural history he knew thoroughly;
he went to the very bottom of things, if
possible, and no one was more conscientious
than he where his knowledge was limited or
merely that of the intelligent layman. His
thorough research in preparing for the African and South American expeditions was not
that of the amateur or of the sportsman but
of the trained naturalist who desires to learn
as much as possible from previous students
and explorers.

The State of New York will erect a splendid
memorial to Theodore Roosevelt the Naturalist and Explorer which will perpetuate the

idealistic and courageous aspects of his character and life as a naturalist. It will adjoin the American Museum of Natural History, which he loved and which inspired him to the activities of his youth and his mature years, where he sought the companionship of men of kindred ambitions and to which he repaired, in the intervals of politics and of pressing duties of every kind, for keen and concentrated discussions on animal coloration, the geographic distribution of mammals and birds, the history of human races, evolution of special groups of animals, and the furtherance of his expeditions. The memorial will remind boys and girls of all generations of Americans of Theodore Roosevelt's spirit of self-effacement, of love, of zeal, of fearlessness, of energy, of intelligence with which they should approach nature in all of its wonderful aspects.

JOHN BURROUGHS—JUNE, 1896

THE TWO JOHNS

JOHN BURROUGHS
1837–1919

JOHN MUIR
1838–1914

"The two Johns," as they were affectionately known by their comrades on the Harriman Expedition to Alaska, were alike in their Christian names, in their love of nature, and, to a certain extent, in their powers of expression, but they were profoundly different in every other respect. I had the privilege of knowing John Muir much more intimately than I knew John Burroughs. I learned through correspondence and through long and intimate conversations thoroughly to understand his Scotch soul, which had a strong Norse element in it and a moral fervor drawn from the Bible of the Covenanters. It is interesting to contrast this Scotch type of soul with the English type of soul seen in John Burroughs.

I had in mind for some time this idea of the racial soul as something more profound in its influence than either the racial temperament or the racial mind. If the body had a long history in the past, so has the soul of man. In reading Wordsworth's noble "Ode on the Intimations of Immortality from Recollections of Early Childhood," it flashed across my mind that along an entirely different path I had reached the same conclusion as Wordsworth: namely, that the human soul is full of reminiscences and that it responds to conditions and experiences long bygone.

THE RACIAL SOUL OF
JOHN BURROUGHS

INDELIBLY stamped on my mind is the celebration of John Burroughs's seventy-fifth birthday in the Bird Hall of the American Museum of Natural History, when six hundred children of the New York East Side schools, Czechs, Hungarians, Poles, Slovaks, no trace of American stock among them, came to tell Burroughs how they loved him and his writings. Twelve bright girls and boys, each representing a volume of the edition of his collected works and wearing the name of the volume suspended in front, came forward and recited a verse or a bit of prose from the volume represented. Tears came into the eyes of "the good gray poet," Burroughs's own designation of Walt Whitman, as the love and admiration of the spirited children poured in upon him. The scene reflected the high purpose of literature, the interpretation of the spiritual and moral influences of nature.

With a large following of grown men, a circle of admirers which included such ex-

tremes as Henry Ford and Theodore Roosevelt, Burroughs was preeminently the poet
of the school children of America, his ability
for humanizing his dumb friends of the animal world having caught the fancy of the
children, thus giving him one of his claims
to immortality in America, if not in other
countries. It was his part in America to
throw the light of nature into the "prison-
house," to use Wordsworth's phrase, which
civilization throws around our youth:

> Heaven lies about us in our infancy!
> Shades of the prison-house begin to close
>   Upon the growing Boy,
> But He beholds the light, and whence it flows,
>   He sees it in his joy;
> The Youth, who daily farther from the east
>   Must travel, still is Nature's Priest,
>   And by the vision splendid
>   Is on his way attended;
> At length the Man perceives it die away,
> And fade into the light of common day.

His fellow poet of nature, John Muir,
though in his way a writer of large imagination, did not humanize his birds and mammals as Burroughs did—a legitimate means
of charming young and old with the habits
and moralities of animal life, provided one

makes it clear that it is an interpretation
and an analogy and not a real resemblance
being pictured. Burroughs loved nature of
the East—of New York and New England
— as Muir, his junior by only a year, cast
over us the spell of the Pacific Coast, from
Alaska to southern California, in all its virgin grandeur. On the voyages to Alaska in
1899 "the two Johns," as they were affectionately called by their companions, met
day by day. Alike in their disregard of conventions, in absent-mindedness in such trivial
matters as clothing and food, and in their
readiness to absorb and to pour out their
nature-philosophy, it would appear that one
steamer was not quite large enough for two
such great men, accustomed as each was, in
his advancing years, to unchecked discourse
and to reverent attention and interest!

In my intimacy with Muir I learned that
his views did not entirely harmonize with
those of Burroughs; the difference was more
or less traceable, I believe, to the Scotch
ancestry of Muir and to his severe and rugged
bringing up as contrasted with the more
equable environment of Burroughs's youth.
Muir chose for observation those aspects of

and suffer nature to entrance us. . . . These en-
chantments are medicinal, they sober and heal
us. (Emerson: "Nature.")

Mounting toward the upland again, I pause
reverently as the hush and stillness of twilight
come upon the woods. It is the sweetest, ripest
hour of the day. And as the hermit's evening
hymn goes up from the deep solitude below me,
I experience that serene exaltation of sentiment
of which music, literature, and religion are but
the faint types and symbols. (Burroughs: "In
the Hemlocks.")

Of the reality of this nature supersense there
is as little doubt as of its rarity.

Burroughs may be called a natural philosopher—a nature-lover more than a naturalist,
for the latter term is reserved for the few
gifted ones, like Darwin and Fabre. His
powers of original observation of nature were
not great powers such as would entitle him
to be called a great naturalist, but powers of
intimate, truthful, and sympathetic observation joined with a love of expression that
made him a prolific producer, and that suggested the title of his first paper, "Expression," published in 1860. The naturalist
instinct has certainly been rare among other
poets and men of letters. Emerson's "Nature," published in 1835, might have been

written at his library table, gazing into the firelight, although his poems, "May-Day," "To the Humble Bee," "The Rhodora," and "Titmouse," are full of the nature vision. Maeterlinck's delightful naturalistic writings are rather the mastery of the observations of Fabre than of a single original observation on his own part. Similarly, the natural philosophy so beautifully expressed by Tennyson in 1850 in his "In Memoriam" was drawn from conversations in a Darwinian club. Wordsworth was richly endowed with the nature supersense, perhaps more so than Burroughs, but he was neither observer, naturalist, nor natural philosopher; he was preeminently the spiritual interpreter. On the other hand, the naturalistic poetry of Erasmus Darwin at the end of the eighteenth century, his "Botanic Garden," his "Loves of the Plants," were the rhythmic expression of original and philosophical thought of a high order. This is true also of Goethe's natural history writings and poetic allusions to nature which sprang from original work in botany and anatomy and brought him near a conception of the theory of evolution a half-century before Charles Darwin.

We look to Gilbert White as one of Burroughs's prototypes in the union of observation and expression, to Izaak Walton in the
joy of outdoor life, and especially to the truly
great Americans, Thoreau and Walt Whitman.
That Burroughs fell under Whitman's influence very early, his poem "Waiting," written
at the age of twenty-five, would seem to
indicate.

My own attention, at the age of twenty-
two, was called to Whitman in a memorable
manner, when he was not considered fit reading for the young. It was in 1879, in the rooms
of Francis Balfour, younger brother of Arthur,
at Cambridge University, where there were
weekly dinners at which one met wits and
celebrities from London and Oxford, as well
as from Cambridge. One evening I was approached by a tall youth with a handsome
face, long hair, flowing collar, and sensuous
mouth, who began immediately to offer an
opinion of American literature. He said:
"You have no real poets in America. To me
Longfellow, Whittier, and the others are mere
echoes of English singers. You Americans
have only one sweet and true songster, whom
you do not appreciate, and that is Walt

Whitman." These words and young Oscar Wilde's appearance are indelibly impressed upon my memory because they first brought home to me the idea that the all-essential quality in a writer of eminence is that he must be of his country, of his soil. This quality, preeminent in Whitman, was possessed in no less degree by Burroughs, although Burroughs was by no means so poetic. Americanism in Americans is essential for the fundamental biological reason that our spiritual and intellectual powers, to reach their highest development, must react to our own environment and not to some other distant or bygone environment. Welcome as British, French, or classical reactions may be among us, they are not of our soil.

These are interpretations of Burroughs's genius, not explanations; we may examine and compare him with other men, but we cannot explain him any more than we can explain the prehistoric artists of the cave period. In each case the genius arrives, assumes leadership, and lifts an entire community of less gifted souls to a little higher level.

This brings us to the sources of the racial soul. Why did the soul of John Burroughs react throughout his life to the genial conditions of our East, to its birds and plants and flowers, to its seasons, to its few retreats still accessible where Nature has preserved some of her unrestrained beauty in her contest with the ruthless destroyer that we call Civilization? Why was he the poet of our robins, of our apple-trees, of the beauties of our forests and farms? Why was he the ardent and sometimes violent prophet of conservation?

Whence the poet's soul, whence the soul of a race, of a people, of a nation? Have we not reason to believe that there is *a racial soul* as well as a racial mind, a racial system of morals, a racial anatomy? This is the thought to which I have been led in trying to penetrate to the inner meaning of the life and works of John Burroughs, because, eager as I am about anatomy, I am far more eager about the origin and development of the moral, spiritual, and intellectual nature of man—the mystery of mysteries in biology at the present time. When Huxley in his Romanes Lecture held that Darwinism fails to throw light on the moral nature of man, he was, in my opinion, wrong; yet the origin of the anatomy and even of the moral nature of man is relatively simple when compared with the origin of the spirit and mind of man. The peculiar mystery about the origin of our spiritual and intellectual powers is that they appear to arise before they are needed—they are ready to play their part before the time and opportunity arise.

Moreover, we have long since abandoned Herbert Spencer's teaching that our spiritual and intellectual faculties are developed through the inherited effects of use, and we now adhere to Weismann's teaching that the use or disuse of our spiritual and intellectual powers has no effect whatever on our offspring, except in so far as it tends to keep us in a normal state of mind and health. The death-blow to Herbert Spencer's view was given in the discoveries of prehistoric art within the last quarter of a century, from which it appears that a race of men of spiritual and intellectual powers arose in which the art spirit had little to do with the struggle for existence and may have run counter to it, as it does at the present time. These discoveries also appear to give pause to the Darwinian theory of the origin of our spiritual and in-

tellectual powers through Natural Selection,
for the periods in man's history and prehis-
tory when the artist or the man of letters
has been best fitted to survive have been few
and far between.

Again, this sudden emergence of our spiritual and intellectual nature from the man of
the environing woods, forests, streams, plains,
and deserts of primeval Asia and Europe
does not favor Bergson's view of the creative
evolution of an internal spiritual and intellectual impulse which must flower out in
time, because if Bergson were right we should
have spiritual and intellectual genius appear-
ing out of season and entirely out of accord
with environment. This is not the case, because there is always an adjustment, a relation, between the internal spiritual and intellectual powers and the external nature of
the time, the beauty or the ugliness, the ease
or the hardship. It is through this reciprocal
relation of the inner man and the environing
world that there are so few misfits. If Bergson were right, our western world would be
full of disharmonies; we should find Mediterranean geniuses springing up in Scandinavian
atmospheres, as is never the case. The *racial*

creative spirit of man always reacts to its own historic racial environment, into the remote past.

Our conclusion is that distinctive spiritual and intellectual powers originate along lines of slow racial evolution in climate and surroundings of distinct kinds. In the south were the Mediterranean lines of migration along sunny seas, formidable enough in the winter season, favorable to rapid development of maritime powers, together with artistic powers, the Mycenæans, the Phœnicians, the early Italian races. The Mediterraneans take nature for granted. In the centre of Europe were the lines of Alpine or Celtic invaders, kept entirely away from the sea, races of agriculturalists and of miners, rich in mechanical talent, neither adventurous nor sea-loving. To the north lived a race of hunters, of seafaring adventurers, resolutely contending with the forces of nature, fond of the open, curious and inquisitive about the causes of things; deliberate in spiritual development, very gradually they reach the greatest intellectual heights and depths.

The racial aptitudes in these three environments of the past twenty thousand years are

now revealed in anatomy and will be no less
clearly revealed in the predispositions of
morals, of intellect, and of spirit. Here nature, religion, and beauty, kept apart by the
superficial vision of man in science, theology,
and æsthetics, are one in the eternal vision
and purpose of the Creator. In the marvelous continuity of heredity a thousand years
are as yesterday.

This is my idea of the origin of the racial
soul, this is my interpretation of Wordsworth's immortal lines:

> Our birth is but a sleep and a forgetting:
> The Soul that rises with us, our life's Star,
>   Hath had elsewhere its setting,
>   And cometh from afar:
>   Not in entire forgetfulness,
>   And not in utter nakedness,
> But trailing clouds of glory do we come
>   From God, who is our home.

Burroughs, the poet of today, found himself at home in the environment of his remote
flint-making ancestors of northern Europe.
The soul that rose with him had its setting
for countless generations in the north; it
came from afar, not in forgetfulness, reflecting and recalling the northern clouds of
nature's glory.

JOHN MUIR

JOHN MUIR

I BELIEVE that John Muir's name is destined to be immortal through his writings on mountains, forests, rivers, meadows and the sentiment of the animal and plant life they contain. I believe that no one else has ever lived with just the same sentiment toward trees and flowers and the works of nature in general as that which John Muir manifested in his life, his conversations and his writings.

In the splendid journey which I had the privilege of taking with him to Alaska in 1896 I first became aware of his passionate love of nature in all its forms and his reverence for it as the direct handiwork of the Creator. He retained from his early religious training under his father this belief, which is so strongly expressed in the Old Testament, that all the works of nature are directly the works of God. In this sense I have never known any one whose nature-philosophy was more thoroughly theistic; at the same time he was a thorough-going evolutionist and always delighted in my own evolutionary studies, which I described to him from time to time in the course of our journeyings and conversations.

It was in Alaska that he quoted the lines from Goethe's "Wilhelm Meister" which inspired all his travels:

> Keep not standing fixed and rooted,
>   Briskly venture, briskly roam;
> Head and hand, where'er thou foot it,
>   And stout heart are still at home.
> In each land the sun doth visit,
>   We are gay whate'er betide,
> To give room for wandering is it
>   That the world was made so wide.

Another sentiment of his regarding trees and flowers always impressed me: that was his attributing to them a personality, an individuality, such as we associate with certain human beings and animals, but rarely with plants. To him a tree was something not only to be loved but to be respected and revered. I well remember his intense indignation over the proposal by his friend Charles S. Sargent to substitute the name *Magnolia fœtida* for *Magnolia grandiflora* on the ground of priority. He quoted Sargent as saying, "After all, 'what's in a name?'" and himself as replying, "There is everything in the name; why inflict upon a beautiful and defenseless plant for all time the stigma of such a name as *Magnolia foetida*? You yourself would not like to have your own name changed from Charles S. Sargent to 'the malodorous Sargent.'"

John Muir's incomparable literary style did not come to him easily, but as the result of the most intense effort. I observed his methods of writing in connection with two of his books upon which he was engaged during the years 1911 and 1912. He came to our home on the Hudson in June, 1911, after the Yale commencement, where he had received the degree of LL.D. on June 21. He brought with him his new silken hood, in which he said he had looked very grand in the commencement parade. On Friday, June 21, he was established in Woodsome Lodge, a log cabin on a secluded mountain height, to complete his volume on the Yosemite. Daily he rose at 4.30 o'clock, and after a simple cup of coffee labored incessantly on his two books, "The Yosemite" and "Boyhood and Youth." It was very interesting to watch how difficult it was for him. In my diary of the time I find the following notes: "Knowing his beautiful and easy style it is very interesting to learn how difficult it is for him; he groans over his labors, he writes and rewrites and interpolates. He loves the simplest English language and admires most of all Carlyle, Emerson, and Thoreau. He is a very firm believer in Thoreau and starts my reading deeply of this author. He also loves his Bible and is constantly quoting it, as well as Milton and Burns. In his attitude toward nature, as well as in his special gifts and abilities, Muir shares many qualities with Thoreau. First among these is his mechanical ability, his fondness for the handling of tools; second, his close identification with nature; third, his interpretation of the religious spirit of nature; fourth, his happiness in solitude with nature; fifth, his lack of sympathy with crowds of people; sixth, his intense love of animals." Thoreau's quiet residence at Walden is to be contrasted with Muir's world-wide journeyings from Scotland to Wisconsin; his penniless journey down the Mississippi to Louisiana, Florida, across Panama, and northward into California in its early grandeur; his establishment of the sawmill, showing again his mechanical ability, as a means of livelihood in the Yosemite; his climbs in the high Sierras and discovery of still living glaciers; his eagerness to see the largest glaciers of Alaska and his several journeys and sojourns there; his wandering all over the great western and eastern forests of the United States; his visits to special forests in Europe; his world tour, without preconceived plan, including the wondrous forests of Africa, Australia, New Zealand and Asia. Finally, his very last great journey.

When starting out on this South American journey, from which I among other friends tried to dissuade him, he often quoted the phrase, "I never turn back." Although he greatly desired to have a comrade on this journey and often urged me to accompany him, he finally was compelled to start out alone, quoting Milton: "I have chosen the lonely way." On July 26 I said good-by to this very dear friend, leaving him to work on his books and prepare for the long journey to South America, especially to see the forests of Araucaria. I know that at this time he had little intention of going on to Africa. It was impulse that led him from the east coast of South America to take a long northward journey in order to catch a steamer for the Cape of Good Hope.

Among the personal characteristics which stand out like crystal in the minds and hearts of his friends were his hatred of shams and his scorn of the conventions of life, his boldness and fearlessness of attack, well illustrated in his assault on the despoilers of the Hetch Hetchy Valley of the Yosemite, whom he loved to characterize as "thieves and robbers." It was a great privilege to be associated with him in this campaign. But certainly his chief characteristic was his intimacy with nature and passionate love of its beauties; also, I believe, his marvelous insight into the creative powers of nature, closely interwoven with his deep religious sentiments and beliefs. Like John Burroughs in many of his characteristics, in others he was totally different, and these differences I attribute to the racial antecedents of the two men, as studied in the "Racial Soul of John Burroughs."

There were published in the New York *Evening Mail* some verses by Charles L. Edson with which I would close this all too brief tribute:

John o' the mountains, wonderful John,
Is past the summit and traveling on:
The turn of the trail on the mountain side,
A smile and "Hail!" where the glaciers slide,
A streak of red where the condors ride,
And John is over the Great Divide.

John o' the mountains camps to-day
On a level spot by the Milky Way;
And God is telling him how He rolled
The smoking earth from the iron mold,
And hammered the mountains till they were cold,
And planted the Redwood trees of old.

And John o' the mountains says: "I knew,
And I wanted to grapple the hand o' you;
And now we're sure to be friends and chums
And camp together till chaos comes."

HOWARD CROSBY BUTLER

HOWARD CROSBY BUTLER
1872–1922

Like Theodore Roosevelt, Butler was a man of many talents and each talent was in the nature of a surprise to his friends. Under his extremely quiet and gentle personality lay force of idealism and of resolution, of courage and persistence which led him to great heights as investigator, teacher, and explorer. It is in respect to this last talent only that this "Impression" is written, because I spoke in the memorial service at Graduate College with others who dwelt on his other talents. As an archæological explorer Butler showed his resourcefulness and powers of command in the most remarkable way. Bedouins, Arabs, native Turks yielded to his quiet and persuasive power, though he rarely raised his voice above a low monotone. Again we turn to the language of Dante and of Homer to express appreciation of this great man.

HOWARD CROSBY BUTLER, EXPLORER

IN the "Divine Comedy," Dante speaks of Ulysses, of exploration of the western seas and lands, of braving dangers, of overcoming obstacles, of offering home, family, friends, life itself, in the quest of the great unknown, its wonders, its beauties, its riches.

"O brothers!" I began, "who to the west
Through perils without number now have reach'd;
To this the short remaining watch, that yet
Our senses have to wake, refuse not proof
Of the unpeopled world, following the track
Of Phœbus. Call to mind from whence ye sprang:
Ye were not form'd to live the lives of brutes,
But virtue to pursue and knowledge high."[1]

For two thousand years our ancestors, thus inspired, were facing the setting sun, until the whole earth had been encircled by explorers. Then, only a brief hundred years ago, the indomitable human spirit turned eastward, toward the rising sun, the Orient, toward the buried treasures and past beauties of the very peoples and civilizations which had been

[1] Dante Alighieri, "Inferno" xxvi, ll. 112-120. Translated by the Reverend H. F. Cary, A.M.

pressing westward from the dawn of history.

Led by Layard, Schliemann, Evans, and a host of others, and chiefly inspired by de Vogué, Howard Crosby Butler became a crusader in this eastward tide of exploration. As a follower in his youthful Princeton days, and in the broad and deep discipline of his graduate years, he prepared himself. A short seven years after graduation, namely, in the year 1899, we find him in the deserts of north central Syria in full command—no longer a follower, but a leader, imaginative, determined, successful, soon becoming distinguished. No one of us who knew the gentle and almost too gentlemanly student of art and the classics under Marquand and Frothingham would have divined his latent powers to command Orientals, whether Arabs, Bedouins, or Turks. *Suaviter in modo, fortiter in re*, he was first trusted, then almost idolized, by his workmen.

It was the sterling integrity, as well as the consummate skill, of Butler's work in Syria (1899-1909) which led to the highest distinction ever offered to an American and Christian explorer by a Mohammedan government, namely, the unsolicited *invitation* to enter and

take command of the excavation of Sardis.
The Turks knew they could trust Butler;
they knew that he was absolutely honorable.
The difficulties of Sardis exploration had
seemed insurmountable to others; the great
period of civilization and culture of Asia
Minor, just older than the Syrian and extending back to the Lydian and beyond, was
buried fathoms deep. These deeply buried
ruins were to be entered under his brilliant
leadership between 1910 and 1922. His was
the secret of self-forgetfulness in a great cause.
He never spoke to us of himself, always of
the workmen, of the colleagues, of the students, of the most beloved Alma Mater. He
was driven on, not by ambition, but by love—
love of his fellow-men, love of his profession,
love of beauty and truth.

Butler's genial and idealistic view of life is
reflected in the characters and personalities
which he brought to life, and now that he has
taken his place among the noble shades of the
long period of 600 B. C. to 600 A. D., the
artisans, the architects, the poets, the mer-
chants, the rulers, the governors, even the
shade of the supreme ruler, Crœsus, will be
grateful to him. We hear them murmuring:

"We have been charged with a mere love of gain and of the gold of Pactolus. You have shown the world that we loved beauty, that we kept our covenants, that we honored our deities." Still more will the shades of ancient Syria and the shades of honorable men and women of the early Christian Church, from its very beginnings beneath the shadows of the ruined pillars of Sardis to the glorious temples of Syria, honor and welcome him.

The span of Butler's life as an explorer was only twenty-two years; his name and his influence will endure as many centuries. So in *our* bereavement we are consoled by *his* immortality.

> . . . That which we are, we are:
> One equal temper of heroic hearts,
> Made weak by time and fate, but strong in will
> To strive, to seek, to find and not to yield.[1]

[1] Alfred Tennyson. "Ulysses." Last four lines.

BIOGRAPHIES BY THE AUTHOR
1883-1924

FRANCIS MAITLAND BALFOUR, Embryologist. *Science*, vol. 2, no. 31, Sept. 7, 1883, pp. 299-301.

ARNOLD GUYOT, Geologist. *The Princetonian*, vol. 8, 1883-84, p. 308.

THOMAS H. HUXLEY, Biologist.

Memorial address before the Biological Section of New York Academy of Sciences, Nov. 11, 1895. *Trans. N. Y. Acad. Sci.*, vol. 15, 1895-96, Sig. dated Jan. 14, 15, 1896, pp. 40-50. *Science*, N. S., vol. 3, no. 57, Jan. 31, 1896, pp. 147-154.

"A Student's Reminiscences of Huxley." Biol. Lectures, Marine Biol. Lab. of Wood's Hole. Ginn & Co., Boston, 1896, pp. 29-42.

G. BROWN GOODE, Zoologist. "Goode as a Naturalist." Address at the G. Brown Goode Memorial Meeting, U. S. National Museum, February 13. *Science*, N. S., vol. 5, no. 114, March 5, 1897, pp. 373-378.

EDWARD DRINKER COPE, Palæontologist.

Memorial Biography. *Science*, N. S., vol. 5, no. 123, May 7, 1897, pp. 705-717.

"A Great Naturalist." *The Century Magazine*, vol. 55, no. 1, Nov. 1897, pp. 10-15.

"Life and Works of Cope." Introduction to Syllabus of Lectures on the Vertebrata by E. D. Cope. Univ. of Penn., 1898, pp. iii-xxxv.

"Work in the Mammals." Address in memory of E. D. Cope, delivered at the meeting in the hall of the American Philosophical Society held in Philadelphia for promoting useful knowledge, Nov. 12,

1897.   *Proc. Amer. Phil. Soc. Memorial Volume I*,
1900, pp. 296-303.

HENRY FILHOL, Palæontologist.   *Science*, N. S., vol. 15,
no. 388, June 6, 1902, p. 912.

KARL ALFRED VON ZITTEL, Palæontologist.   *Science*,
N. S., vol. 19, no. 474, Jan. 29, 1904, pp. 186-188.

JOHN BELL HATCHER, Palæontologist.   "Explorations
of John Bell Hatcher for the Palæontological Monographs of the U. S. Geological Survey, together
with a statement of his contributions to American
Geology and Palæontology." Monographs of the
U. S. Geol. Survey, vol. 49, "The Ceratopsia" by
Hatcher, Marsh, Lull. Washington, 1907, pp. 17-26.

MORRIS KETCHAM JESUP, Administrator.
Science, N. S., vol. 27, no. 684, Feb. 7, 1908, pp. 235-
236.

Address of Welcome at commemoration of the found-
ing of the American Museum of Natural History.
Unveiling of the statue of Morris K. Jesup.   *Amer.
Mus. Journ.*, vol. 10, March, 1910, pp. 60-67.

CHARLES DARWIN, Biologist.
"Remarks on Darwin."   *The Evening Post*, New
York, Feb. 12, 1909, p. 3.

"Darwin Celebrations in the United States."   *Nature*,
vol. 80, No. 2055, March 18, 1909, pp. 72-73.

"Life and Works of Darwin."   Address delivered
Feb. 12, 1909, at Columbia University on the
hundredth anniversary of Darwin's birth, Feb. 12,
1809, as the first of a series of nine lectures on
"Charles Darwin and His Influence on Science."
Pop. Sci. Monthly, vol. 74, no. 4, April, 1909, pp.
313-343.

"Acceptance of the Portrait of Darwin."   *Ann.
N. Y. Acad. Sci.*, vol. 19, no. 1, pt. 1, July 31, 1909,
pp. 21-22.

"The Darwin Centenary."   Address in reply to the
reception of delegates, Cambridge, England, June

23, 1909. *Science*, N. S., vol. 30, no. 763, Aug. 13, 1909, pp. 199-200.

JOHN I. NORTHROP, Zoologist. Introduction to "A Naturalist in the Bahama Islands." A memorial volume. 8vo. Columbia University Press, June 15, 1910, 276 pp.

ALFRED RUSSEL WALLACE, Naturalist.
"Scientific Worthies." *Nature*, vol. 89, no. 2224, June 13, 1912, pp. 367-370.
"Alfred Russel Wallace, 1823-1913." *Pop. Sci. Monthly*, vol. 83, no. 6, pp. 523-537.
"A Great Naturalist." *Amer. Mus. Journ.*, vol. 13, no. 8, pp. 331-333.

JOSEPH LEIDY, Anatomist. Biographical Memoir. Read by title at meeting of National Academy of Sciences, April 18-20, 1911. Presented to the Academy at the April Meeting, 1912. *Biographical Memoirs National Acad. of Sciences*, part of vol. 7, Feb., 1913, pp. 339-396.

LOUIS PASTEUR, Bacteriologist. "The New Order of Sainthood." *The Churchman*, vol. 107, no. 15 (whole no. 3560), April 12, 1913, pp. 474-475. Reprinted by Charles Scribner's Sons, 12mo, October, 1913, 17 pp.

EBERHARD FRASS, Palæontologist. *Science*, N. S., vol. 41, no. 1059, April 16, 1915, pp. 571-572.

JOHN MUIR, Naturalist. *Sierra Club Bulletin*, vol. 10, no. 1, January, 1916, pp. 29-32.

GUSTAV SCHWALBE, Anatomist. *Science*, N. S., vol. 44, no. 1125, July 21, 1916, p. 97.

JOEL ASAPH ALLEN, Zoologist.
Foreword to "Autobiographical Notes and a Bibliography of the Scientific Publications of Joel Asaph Allen." *Amer. Mus. Nat. Hist. Publ.*, 8vo, Dec. 26, 1916, xi and 215 pp.
"An Appreciation." *Nat. Hist.*, vol. 21, pp. 513-515.

WILLIAM BERRYMAN SCOTT, Palæontologist. "The

Work of Professor William Berryman Scott '77." *The Princeton Alumni Weekly*, vol. 17, no. 10, Dec. 5, 1917, pp. 225-226.

JOSEPH HODGES CHOATE, Lawyer. A Tribute from the Trustees of the American Museum. *Mus. Publ.* 4to, June 25, 1918, 34 pp.

THEODORE ROOSEVELT, Explorer.

"Colonel Roosevelt." *The (New York) Evening Post*, vol. 118, no. 41, p. 7, Jan. 6, 1919.

"Theodore Roosevelt, Naturalist." *Nat. Hist.*, vol. 19, no. 1, March 28, 1919, pp. 9-10.

"Roosevelt the Student of Nature." *The New York Sun*, vol. 89, no. 55, Nov. 3, 1921, p. 24.

SAMUEL WENDELL WILLISTON, Palæontologist.

Journ. of Geol., vol. 26, no. 8, Nov.-Dec., 1918, pp. 673-689. *Science*, N. S., vol. 49, no. 1264, pp. 274-278, March 21, 1919. *Bull. Geol. Soc. of Amer.*, vol. 30, pp. 66-76.

"Samuel Wendell Williston—The man and the palæontologist." *Sigma Xi Quart.*, vol. 7, no. 1, July 19, 1919, pp. 2-6.

JAMES BRYCE, Author. Address on Viscount Bryce at the Memorial Service in the Cathedral of St. John the Divine, March 5, 1922.

JOHN BURROUGHS, Naturalist. "The Racial Soul of John Burroughs." Address at the Memorial Meeting of the American Academy of Arts and Letters, November 18, 1921.

HOWARD CROSBY BUTLER, Archæologist. Address at the Memorial Meeting in Graduate College, Princeton University, October 21, 1922.